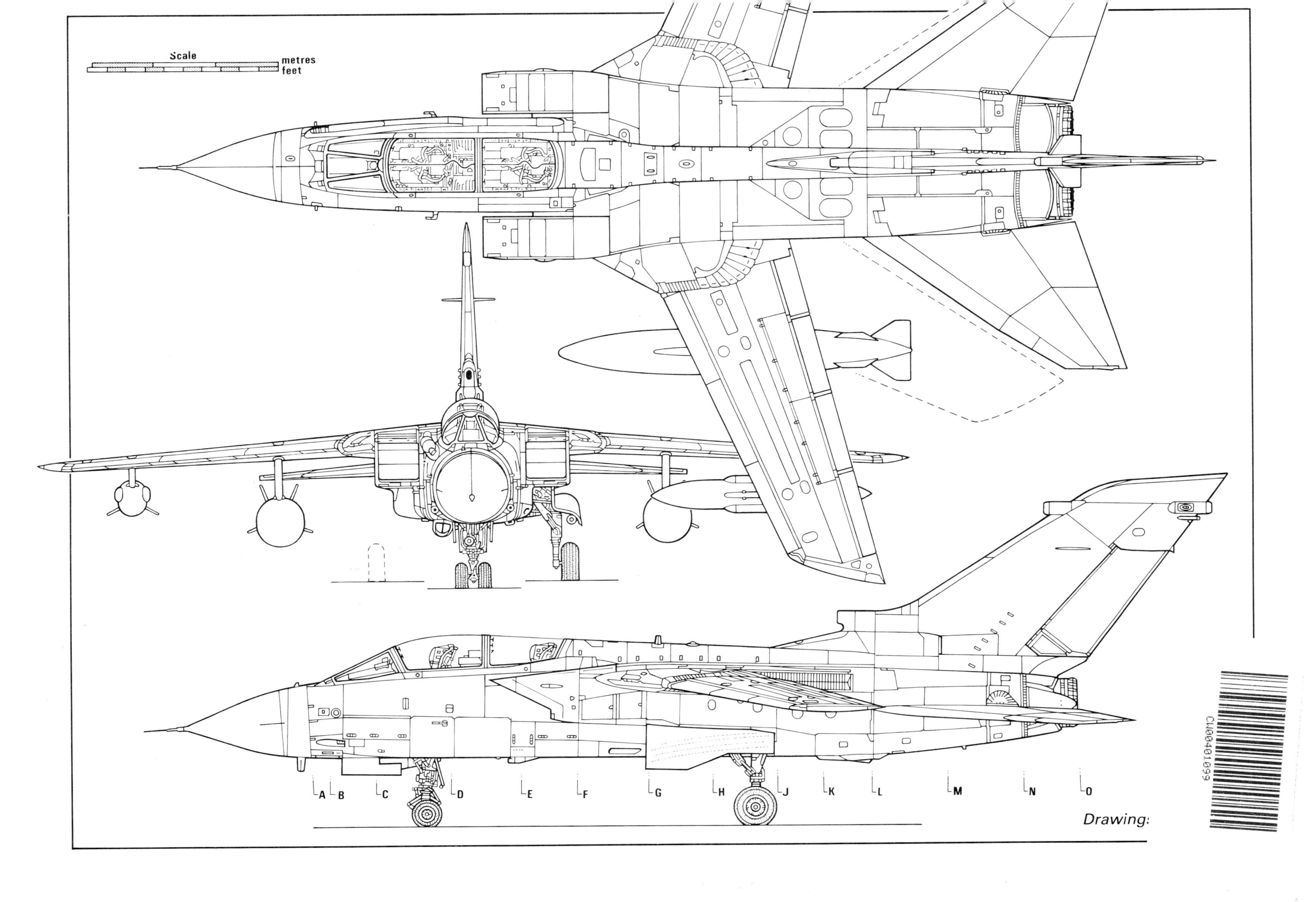
Scale
metres
feet
A
B
C
D
E
F
G
H
J
K
L
M
N
O
Drawing:

PANAVIA TORNADO

Below:
Tornado GR1 ZA595 'K' of No 9 Squadron, pictured at Honington in September 1982. *RAF Official*

PANAVIA TORNADO

SPEARHEAD OF NATO

Dr ALFRED PRICE FR Hist S

LONDON

IAN ALLAN LTD

Contents

Below:
A No 9 Squadron GR1 waits for the word to taxi out for a 'Green Flag' mission.
Frank Mormillo

Unless otherwise credited, the illustrations in this book are the copyright of the manufacturing companies on the Tornado programme.

First published 1988

ISBN 0 7110 1726 3

Published by Ian Allan Ltd, Shepperton, Surrey; and printed by Ian Allan Printing Ltd at their works at Coombelands in Runnymede, England

Author's Preface

Having been commissioned to write and illustrate this book on the Tornado, I discussed it with Folkhard Oelwein, head of Panavia's public relations department. Of course he was pleased that someone planned to write about his company's product and, being a convinced European, gently made the point that such an account could not possibly do justice to the subject unless it described the development of the Tornado from the viewpoint of all three nations involved. Folkhard, together with David Kamiya at Warton, Piero Vergnano at Turin and Wolfram Wolff at Ottobrunn, kindly arranged interviews with senior executives in their companies. At the same time Oberst Geissinger and Colonelo de Carolis, respectively the German and Italian Air Attachés in London, and Air Commodore Robson, the Director of Royal Air Force Public Relations, arranged for me to conduct interviews at service airfields operating Tornados in the three countries. I am deeply grateful to these gentlemen for their assistance, and to Sidgwick & Jackson Ltd for permission to use material assembled for my book, *Air Battle Central Europe*. The account which follows depends heavily on the material supplied by the interviewees listed at the end of this Preface, but I alone am responsible for those views which have not been directly attributed to anyone else. Unless otherwise stated, the passages quoted verbatim are taken from transcripts of tape recordings I made during the interviews.

One problem with researching a book on a modern combat aircraft is that much of the information has to come from the makers. Before I visited the companies I half expected to find myself speaking to a succession of people all pushing the corporate line that development of the Tornado had gone off without a hitch, that everything had been perfect in every way. That was certainly not the case, however, and I was pleasantly surprised at the frankness of the replies to many of my questions. As a result I have been able to write an account which casts new light not only on the Tornado, but also on the design and development of modern combat aircraft and on the nature of international co-operative ventures.

October 1987

Alfred Price
Uppingham
Rutland

The Witnesses

It would have been impossible to write this book had it not been for the wholehearted co-operation of a large number of those involved in the Tornado programme, and the author wishes to convey his gratitude to the following (in each case the posts and service ranks were those held at the time of their interview by the author);

Karl-Heinz Artelt, Chief Navigator, MBB Manching.
Tenentecolonelo Paolo Baroni, Senior Engineer Officer 6° Stormo, Italian Air Force Ghedi.
Generalmajor Heinz Birkenbeil, German Air Force (retired).
Wing Commander Richard Bogg, Officer Commanding No 31 Squadron, Royal Air Force Brüggen.
Umberto Bonaccino, Aeritalia Turin.
Capitano Sergio Burini, 6° Stormo, Italian Air Force Ghedi.
Dr Ing Giandomenico Cantele, Director Combat Aircraft Group, Aeritalia Turin.
Fausto Certeti, President, Aeritalia Rome.
Colonelo Marcello Conti, Officer Commanding 6° Stormo, Italian Air Force Ghedi.
Squadron Leader Peter Dunlop, No 617 Squadron, Royal Air Force Marham.
David Eagles, Chief Test Pilot, British Aerospace Warton.
Group Captain Michael Elsam, Commanding Officer, Royal Air Force Coningsby.
Generale di Divisione Aerea Rolando Goldoni, Italian Air Ministry, Rome.
Generale Ispettore Prof. Ing Licio Giorgieri, Italian Air Ministry, Rome.
Generale da Brigatta Lorenzo Gioru, Commanding Officer 1st Air Region, Italian Air Force.
Wing Commander Peter Gooding, Royal Air Force, Ministry of Defence, London.
Korvettenkapitän Konstantin Henkel, Marine Flieger Geschwader 1, German Navy Jagel.
Dipl.Ing Albrecht Herold, Programme Manager Tornado, MBB Ottobrunn.
Air Marshal Sir Patrick Hine, Commander in Chief Royal Air Force Germany, RAF Rheindahlen.
Oberstleutnant Walter Jertz, Jagdbombergeschwader 31, German Air Force Noervenich.
Oberstleutnant Klaus Kahlert, Jagdbombergeschwader 31, German Air Force, Noervenich.
Hans-Joachim Klapperich-Andress, Managing Director, Panavia Munich.
Richard Kleebaur, Sales Engineer, Panavia Munich.
Peter Klein, Dipl.-Ing, Vice President, MBB Dynamics, Ottobrunn.
Karl Knauer, Dipl.-Ing, Project Director, Panavia Munich.
Fregattenkapitän Volke Liche, Marine Flieger Geschwader 1, German Navy Jagel.
Peter Liddell, Manager Advanced Projects, British Aerospace Warton.
Squadron Leader Andrew Lister-Tomlinson, No 229 OCU, Royal Air Force Coningsby.
Professor Gero Madelung, MBB Ottobrunn.
Wing Commander Grant McLeod, Officer Commanding No 17 Squadron, Royal Air Force Brüggen.
Fregattenkapitaen Wolf Merlich, Senior Engineering Officer Marine Flieger Geschwader 1, German Navy Jagel.
Flight Lieutenant Richard Middleton, No 617 Squadron, Royal Air Force Marham.
Paul Millett, Chief Executive, British Aircraft Corporation, Riyadh, Saudi Arabia.
Wing Commander Richard Peacock-Edwards, Officer Commanding No 229 OCU, Royal Air Force Coningsby.
Hauptmann Hans-Dieter Poth, Jagdbombergeschwader 31, German Air Force Noervenich.
Hansfriedrich Rammenseé, Chief Test Pilot, MBB Manching.
Kenneth Simpson, Regional Marketing Manager, Panavia Munich.
Air Vice-Marshal Tony Skingsley, Assistant Chief of Air Staff Royal Air Force, Ministry of Defence, London.
Dipl.-Ing Martin Steinberger, Turbo-Union Munich.
John Wittaker, Head of Reprographics Department, British Aerospace Warton.
John Vincent, Project Manager Experimental Aircraft Programme, Warton.
John Waite, Head of Technical Management, British Aerospace Warton.
Brian Young, Technical Director Military Aircraft Division, British Aerospace.

Prologue

Ellsworth Air Force Base, South Dakota, USA: 6.25am on the morning of 10 October 1984. From the cockpit of his Tornado attack aircraft lined up for take-off at one end of the main runway, Sqn Ldr Peter Dunlop of No 617 Squadron, Royal Air Force, peers into the gloom beyond his canopy. With visibility about 30yd in fog he can just make out the furry glow of two runway lights on either side to confirm that the aircraft is correctly aligned. Thus assured he releases the brakes and pushes open the throttles. With a crackling roar the two engines spool up to maximum thrust and the machine accelerates rapidly into the translucent swirl. When the Tornado reaches 145kt Dunlop eases back on the stick and the aircraft lifts cleanly into the air.

This is a flight into the unknown, in more than one sense. The sortie is one of those for the US Air Force's Strategic Air Command bombing competition, the most prestigious event of its kind in the world and the military aeronautical equivalent of the Olympic Games. Dunlop and his navigator are one of four Tornado crews of No 617 Squadron pitting their skills against 38 crews from other services: crews flying B-52s and FB-111s of Strategic Air Command, and F-111s of US Tactical Air Command, US Air Forces Europe and the Royal Australian Air Force. In the face of such strong competition it will be no disgrace to turn in a score that secures a place in the middle of the pack: the competing crews are the most capable and experienced their respective forces can muster and they are operating some of the most advanced bombing and navigation equipment in existence. It is the first year the Tornado has taken part in the competition and the new type is thought to have little chance of success against such tough opposition: it is by far the smallest of the aircraft competing and No 617 Squadron has completed its conversion training on to the new type only six months earlier.

Once airborne, Dunlop climbs his aircraft through the fog layer into the blue skies above and, with Flt Lt Dick Middleton in the rear cockpit operating the radar and navigation systems, makes his way via the planned zig-zag route to the first objective: a simulated bombing attack from 19,000ft against a target near Powell, Wyoming, to be carried out at 8.17am, exactly 112min after take-off. The attack run is tracked by a radar on the ground to assess bombing and timing accuracy, and the crew will lose points for aiming errors and for each second early or late. The 'attack' seems to go well, though the Tornado crew will not learn how well until the official scores are announced three weeks later: 147 out of 150 points for bombing accuracy, 49 out of 50 points for timing.

After its first attack the Tornado has to rendezvous with a Victor tanker, to take on the fuel necessary for it to continue the sortie. The transfer takes 10min, then Dunlop eases back on the throttles and the aircraft descends for the low altitude phase of the sortie — and back into the layer of fog close to the ground.

Dunlop levels the Tornado 700ft above the ground and switches in the automatic pilot. Under Middleton's control the electronic navigation system holds the aircraft at that altitude and flies it accurately towards the next target near South Big Horn, Wyoming. Had it been a war sortie the Tornado would be flying at 200ft, but the bomb-scoring radar on the ground cannot give continuous tracking on aircraft flying that low. This part of the flight could be a severe test of the crew's confidence in the automatic navigation equipment: the route to the target takes them between ranges of mountains which tower more than 5,000ft above the aircraft on either side, menacing but invisible in the fog. Nevertheless, these are highly-trained and professional crewmen, who know their aircraft's capabilities; and despite the poor visibility the attack at 9.53am scores the maximum possible points: 200 out of 200.

The third target is near Gillett, Wyoming, and the attack at 10.24am secures more perfect scores: 200 out of 200 for bombing and 50 out of 50 for timing. Afterwards Dunlop takes the Tornado to 15,000ft for its second rendezvous with a Victor tanker to take on more fuel. This task complete, the Tornado returns to low altitude for the last two bombing runs; by now the fog is starting to thin. The fourth target, near Wiboux, Montana, is attacked at 11.08am (bomb score 198 out of 200); the fifth, near Scoby, Montana, is attacked at 11.29am (bomb score 192 out of 200, timing score 50 out of 50). After the last attack Dunlop climbs to 16,000ft and heads back to Ellsworth. The Tornado lands at 12.15pm, 5hr 50min after take-off.

That was the second of three competition sorties which the crew had to fly. Peter Dunlop described his feelings after he and Middleton completed their third such sortie:

'Everything we had planned had come right. Our radar offset points had come up on the screen as expected, we

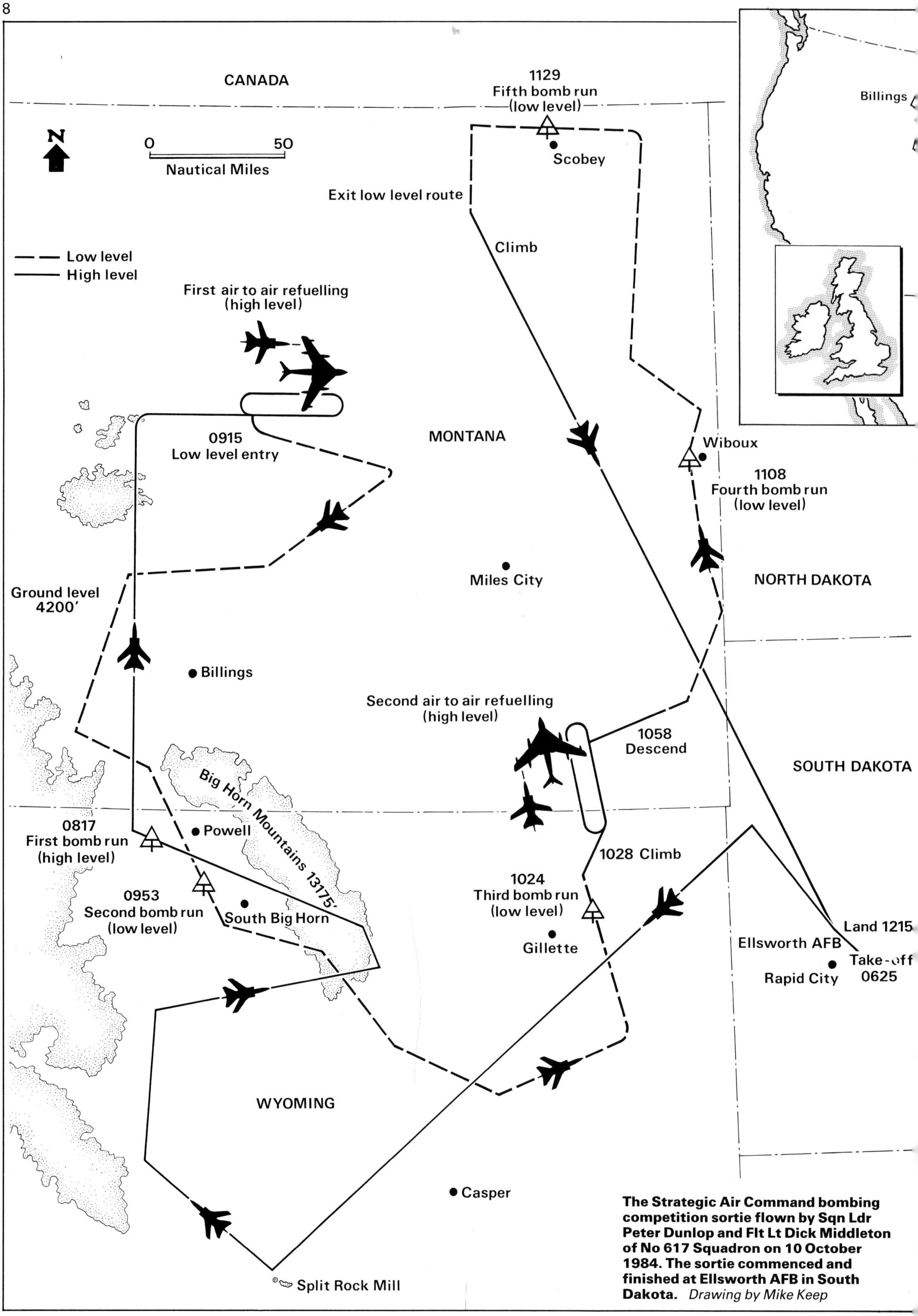

CANADA
1129
Fifth bomb run
(low level)
Billings
N
0 50
Nautical Miles
Scobey
Exit low level route
Climb
Low level
High level
First air to air refuelling
(high level)
0915
Low level entry
MONTANA
Wiboux
1108
Fourth bomb run
(low level)
Miles City
NORTH DAKOTA
Ground level
4200′
Billings
Second air to air refuelling
(high level)
1058
Descend
SOUTH DAKOTA
Big Horn Mountains 13175′
0817
First bomb run
(high level)
Powell
1028 Climb
1024
Third bomb run
(low level)
0953
Second bomb run
(low level)
South Big Horn
Gillette
Land 1215
Ellsworth AFB
Take-off
0625
Rapid City
WYOMING
Casper
Split Rock Mill

The Strategic Air Command bombing competition sortie flown by Sqn Ldr Peter Dunlop and Flt Lt Dick Middleton of No 617 Squadron on 10 October 1984. The sortie commenced and finished at Ellsworth AFB in South Dakota. *Drawing by Mike Keep*

Above left:
Dunlop and Middleton's sortie of 10 October in geographical perspective. The 5hr 50min flight covered an area almost as great as the United Kingdom. *Drawing by Mike Keep*

Above:
A Tornado of No 617 Squadron turns in to land at Ellsworth AFB in September 1984, during a training mission for the Strategic Air Command bombing competition.

Above:
Moment of victory: members of the No 617 Squadron team looking rather pleased with themselves, as the result of the Meyer Trophy is announced at Barksdale AFB on 31 October 1984. With arms raised in the centre of the photograph are, left to right, Sqn Ldr Peter Dunlop, Flt Lt Dick Middleton and Flt Lt Iain Hunter.

Below:
Sweeping the board: part of the No 617 Squadron team pictured with the trophies won during the competition. From left to right are Peter Dunlop and Dick Middleton pictured with the Le May trophy; centre is Wg Cdr Tony Harrison, Squadron Commander, with the Tornado Trophy awarded to the crew getting the best overall score flying this aircraft, won by Dunlop and Middleton; and on the right are Flt Lt Dermot Dolan and Flt Lt Iain Hunter with the Meyer Trophy for the best score by a two-aircraft team of Tornados, F-111s or FB-111s.

had not missed a single timing point, we had met each tanker aircraft in the right place at the right time. It is not often one can return from a sortie and, after reflection, say that one could not have done a single thing any better. We had flown three sorties like that, with a total of more than 18 hours airborne. Nothing had gone wrong with any of our aircraft, there had not been even the most minor failure. Before the results were announced Dick and I were quietly confident we would get a good place. I said to him "If any other crew has done better than we have, they bloody well deserve to win!" '

Peter Dunlop's optimism was not misplaced. During the three sorties he and Dick Middleton had scored 2,616 points out of a possible 2,650, which won for them the Curtis E. Le May Bombing Trophy for the individual crew gaining the highest score. This success for the Tornado was no fluke: another crew from No 617 Squadron, Flt Lt Steve Legge and Sqn Ldr Vic Bussereau, gained second place for the Le May Trophy. For the Mathis Trophy, awarded for the best two-aircraft team, pairs of Tornados gained second and sixth places. And for the John C. Meyer Trophy, for which eight pairs of F-111s and Tornados competed, the latter took first and third places.

At the time of writing the Tornado multi-role combat aircraft is firmly established in the air forces of Great Britain, Italy and Germany and in the German Navy; it has been ordered for the Saudi Arabian and Omani Air Forces and orders are in prospect from other governments. Given the military and commercial success of the programme, some readers might find it difficult to believe there was a time when there were grave doubts in military aviation circles on the wisdom of building such an aircraft. Yet that was indeed the case. To realise the importance of those events in the autumn of 1984 we must look at what had gone before, from the beginning of the Tornado programme almost exactly 17 years earlier.

The Tornado was conceived, more in hope than in certainty, as an exercise in European military and industrial co-operation. The programme was borne with misgivings, nurtured in scepticism and during its adolescence suffered a powerful campaign of denigration which nearly led to its downfall. Many people felt it was an attempt to build a 'Jack of all trades' aircraft that would be a master of none. Yet while this was going on, dedicated teams of clever people were working behind closed doors to design and build an aircraft that would confound the critics. As Tornados began to emerge from the factories they demonstrated the true capabilities of the aircraft. Gradually an undercurrent of opinion in support of Tornado began to develop beyond those in company and military circles whose future careers depended on the success of the programme. As more and more service pilots and navigators flew the aircraft — and these were men unlikely to gloss over its failings as the maker's employees might — they saw for themselves that the Tornado was an extremely effective attack aircraft which could hit its targets with precision at night or in almost any weather. In the summer of 1983 the first operational Tornado squadrons completed their conversion training and took part in NATO exercises; pilots of air defence fighters had grudgingly to admit that it was very hard to catch these new aircraft able to fly fast and low in darkness or poor visibility.

Yet outside service circles there were still doubts about the Tornado, for prejudice dies hard. The need was for unequivocal and public signs that this innovative European tri-national venture really had produced an effective combat aircraft. No 617 Squadron's success in the SAC Bombing Competition in October 1984 provided one such sign; it demonstrated that in one of the most difficult combat aircraft roles, that of precision low altitude attack at night or in bad weather, the Tornado is at least as good as any other aircraft type in existence. The orders for the aircraft from Saudi Arabia and Oman, gained in the face of strong international competition, provided another such sign. These and other developments have triumphantly vindicated those who, at the beginning of the programme, had staked their reputations on its success as part of the grand design they had perceived for a more united Europe.

Below:
Under cover: Tornado GR1 ZA607 'P' of No 617 Squadron is seen here in its Hardened Aircraft Shelter.

1 The Nations Come Together

On 19 October 1967 the Chiefs of Staff of the Dutch, Belgian, German and Italian Air Forces met at Fürstenfeldbruch near Munich for tentative discussions on a common aircraft to replace the F-104 Starfighters in their respective services. That meeting can be regarded as the starting point for the Tornado programme, though none of those present could know how different the resultant aircraft would be from the one they were considering. The officers agreed to form a Joint Working Group to examine each service's requirements and draw up specifications for an aircraft to meet these. Shortly afterwards the Canadian Armed Forces asked to join the Working Group and were accepted into it.

In the case of the F-104 the five nations had adapted to their requirements an American design which their respective aircraft industries built under licence. That was the least risky way of securing a replacement aircraft, but the European nations were anxious to develop their aircraft industries and the best way to do that was to have them design and build a combat aircraft on their own. Lt-Col Heinz Birkenbeil, then working in the requirements branch of the German Air Ministry, summed up the mood:

'Buy American, that was always an argument. But there was a strong feeling that we had to build up a European capability to build our own combat aircraft. We had enough money, we had enough people, we had enough knowledge. It was felt that if several nations worked together we could build such an aircraft, whereas working alone the nations could do nothing.'

Since the renaissance of the German aircraft industry in the 1950s there had been several attempts to design and build a modern combat aircraft. The result was a string of projects, most of which never flew and none of which went into production, usually on the grounds of cost. The other nations had faced similar experiences.

Throughout these early discussions, aircraft companies from nations outside the Joint Working Group fought hard to get one of their designs accepted as the F-104 replacement. As might be expected from the nation which had produced the Starfighter and had come to regard its replacement almost as an extension of its home market, the American industry mounted a strong campaign. Lockheed offered its projected CL-1200 Lancer fighter developed from the earlier aircraft, with many common structural components but with a larger engine to beef up the all-round performance (it never flew). Northrop offered its P530 design which it pushed hard as the aircraft that could best fulfil the mission requirements. 'The P530 was something else', one of those monitoring the discussions later commented, 'it seemed to benefit from a different set of laws of physics to other aeroplanes; it offered an enormous performance for an unbelievably low weight'. (With some changes the P530 later flew as the F-17 which did not go into production; the later and much heavier F-18 developed from it has been produced in large numbers and is a successful air superiority fighter and daylight attack aircraft.) From France, Dassault offered a development of its Mirage F.1 fighter. And from Sweden the SAAB company offered its Viggen multi-role combat aircraft. But the nations in the Joint Working Group were keen to exhaust the possibilities of having their own industries build the new aircraft before they sought a design from outside.

In general terms the five air forces were looking for a small and relatively inexpensive multi-purpose fighter-bomber with an operational take-off weight of 25,000-30,000lb (about the same as the F-104). There was, however, a complicating factor. During the 1960s NATO had abandoned the doctrine that it would answer any incursion by Warsaw Pact forces into its territory with a massive nuclear retaliation. Instead there was the new doctrine of flexible response: unless enemy forces made first use of nuclear weapons, initially such an incursion would be countered by conventional forces and nuclear weapons would be used only as a last resort. This shift in tactical doctrine had a fundamental impact on the requirements of the new combat aircraft: it would need to be able to carry a much greater weight of high explosive bombs, and deliver them far more accurately than was possible for the F-104. The need to fulfil these additional demands — or rather the different air forces' interpretations of how they should be achieved — would come close to wrecking the programme.

To cover everybody's requirements the aircraft would have had to be able to fly in the air superiority, interception, close air support, interdiction and reconnaissance roles, and a two-seat version would be needed for conversion training. Within these roles, however, most nations had specific requirements of their own.

The German Air Force requirement would best have been met by the NKF design (*Neues Kampfflugzeug* — new combat aircraft) from the Messerschmitt-Bölkow-Blohm group of companies — which the German government had said it could not afford as a single-nation development. The NKF was to have been a single-seat, single-engined swing-winged aircraft with a take-off weight of 31,500lb, capable of Mach 1 at low altitude and Mach 1.5 at 36,000ft and suitable for the close air support, air superiority, shallow interdiction and reconnaissance roles. In the close air support role the aircraft would carry a 4,000lb payload to a combat operating radius of 200 miles; or, in the interdictor role, it would carry 2,500lb to a target 325 miles from its base; for the air superiority role the aircraft would carry four air-to-air missiles and have a combat radius of 200 miles. Because the German Air Force expects its airfields to come under attack in time of war, the aircraft had to be able to take-off within a ground roll of 1,500ft and land within 1,000ft. The avionics had not been specified in detail, but had the aircraft been built it would probably have been capable of attack operations only by day and in good weather.

The Italian Air Force's ideas for a F-104 replacement had not been defined to the same extent, but they pointed towards a rather different aircraft. Essentially, the Italians were thinking of a high performance interceptor able to exceed Mach 2 at 60,000ft; the aircraft was also to have secondary roles of air superiority, shallow interdiction and close air support, with the ability to carry a 16,000lb bomb load over short distances.

The Canadians had different ideas still: they were looking for a high performance dogfighter with extremely good manoeuvrability and a very high thrust-to-weight ratio, with a secondary ground attack capability.

In July 1968 the Royal Air Force became a member of the Joint Working Group. As an additional member to the programme Britain was welcomed, especially as it brought with it a large national aircraft industry with considerable recent experience in the design, construction and production of combat aircraft. Against this the new member introduced a lot of new problems for those trying to draw up a common specification, for the RAF wanted a larger and more complex aircraft than those previously considered.

To understand the RAF position it is necessary to outline that service's re-equipment programme as it stood in the summer of 1968. Earlier in the decade it had planned to replace its Canberras and V-bombers with TSR2 long-range, low-altitude interdictor-strike aircraft; but the TSR2 suffered huge cost overruns and the programme was cancelled in 1965 shortly after the prototype began flight trials. The intended replacement for TSR2 was a swing-winged aircraft to be built jointly with France, provisionally called the AFVG (Anglo-French Variable Geometry). As a stop-gap, until the AFVG

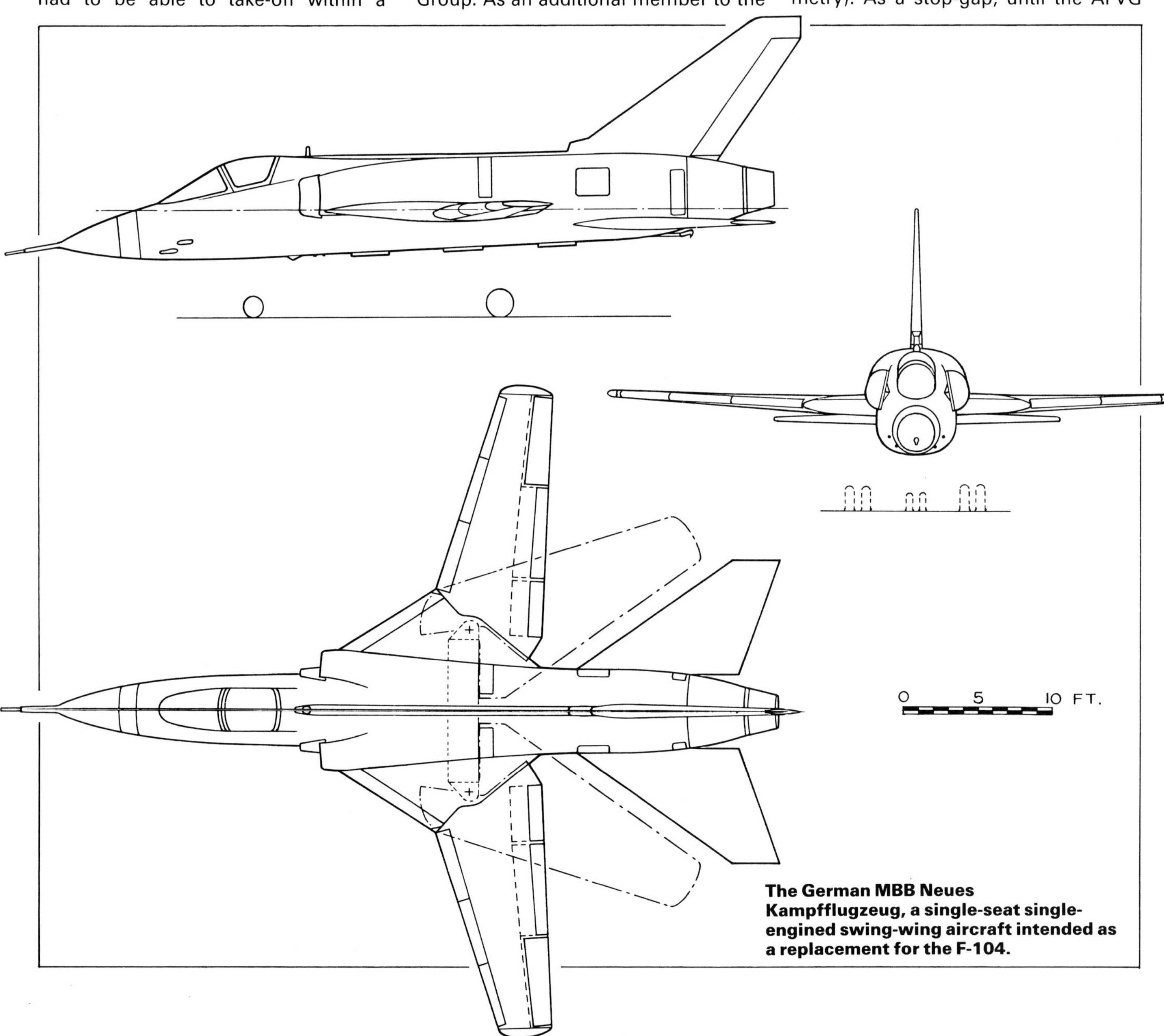

The German MBB Neues Kampfflugzeug, a single-seat single-engined swing-wing aircraft intended as a replacement for the F-104.

became available, in 1966 the British Government ordered 50 General Dynamics F-111 swing-wing attack aircraft from America. The French never had their hearts in the AFVG project and after about a year they pulled out of it. The AFVG was renamed the UKVG and the British Aircraft Corporation (BAC) continued working on it, but the Government made it clear there would be no orders unless a foreign government agreed to share the development costs. Then in 1968, a financial crisis forced the British Government to cancel the order for the F-111s.

For the RAF it had been a traumatic series of events: vast sums of money had been spent without a single combat aircraft to show for it. As a stop-gap measure to replace the obsolete Canberras in its strike/attack squadrons, that service bought the best off-the-shelf aircraft then available: Buccaneers and F-4 Phantoms. Neither aircraft was a new design and both would need replacing in the 1980s, as would the ageing Vulcan bombers which now had to continue in service long after they should have been pensioned off.

The RAF entered the Joint Working Group with a clear idea of the sort of aircraft it needed most: a two-seat, long-range, low-altitude strike/attack aircraft with the avionics necessary for night and all-weather operations — that amounted to a F-111, or as near to one as it could talk the other partners into accepting. Also, though it kept the requirement secret at the time, that service was also looking for a long-range interceptor to replace the Phantom in its air defence squadrons and it was hoped a variant of the new aircraft might be suitable for this role.

Above:
A mock-up of the AFVG at Warton.

One of the first RAF officers involved with the Joint Working Group was Wg Cdr Tony Skingsley, then head of the Operational Requirements 13 Branch at the Ministry of Defence in London.

'Once we went into the venture we were looking at how we could put together a collaborative requirement. And since the other countries were interested in a much smaller aeroplane, a F-111-sized aircraft was clearly not on. On precedent the United Kingdom would have built its own aeroplane, but the Government had stated publicly that Britain was not going to build the aircraft alone. That made it very difficult for us to negotiate terms: it is not easy to negotiate when one's Government has said there is no national fall-back position on the matter. The other nations had never developed a modern combat aeroplane; they had all bought the F-104 design off the shelf and built it under licence. They wanted to develop an aircraft of their own but they knew their industries lacked the capability to do it. They knew they would have to collaborate with somebody, the British or the French or the Americans. So there was pressure for a collaborative development on their part, and there was political pressure on our part to do it. Those pressures forced us together.'

Soon after the British Government entered the programme the six nations signed a Memorandum of Understanding to draw up a common specification for a combat aircraft to meet the needs of their air forces. The new aircraft was designated the MRA-75 (Multi-Role Aircraft for 1975). If the programme fulfilled its most optimistic predictions the number of aircraft required would be huge: the German Air Force and Navy were talking of 600 aircraft, the Royal Air Force 385, the Belgians and the Dutch about 240 each, the Italians 200 and the Canadians about 150: a total of 1,815 aircraft. The MRA-75 was to be built in both single-seat and two-seat versions, the latter for conversion training and to meet the RAF requirement.

In previous international combat aircraft programmes one nation had assumed the role of leader and the other nations adopted a supporting role. For example, in the case of the BAC-Breguet Jaguar attack aircraft, the Dassault-Breguet Atlantic maritime patrol aircraft and the Aérospatiale-MBB-Fokker Transall freighter, the French led these programmes and the other nations helped finance them and build components. Similarly, in previous co-operative programmes between the USA and Europe, the Americans had always been the lead nation. On the basis of their stated requirement the Germans were by far the largest customer for the new aircraft

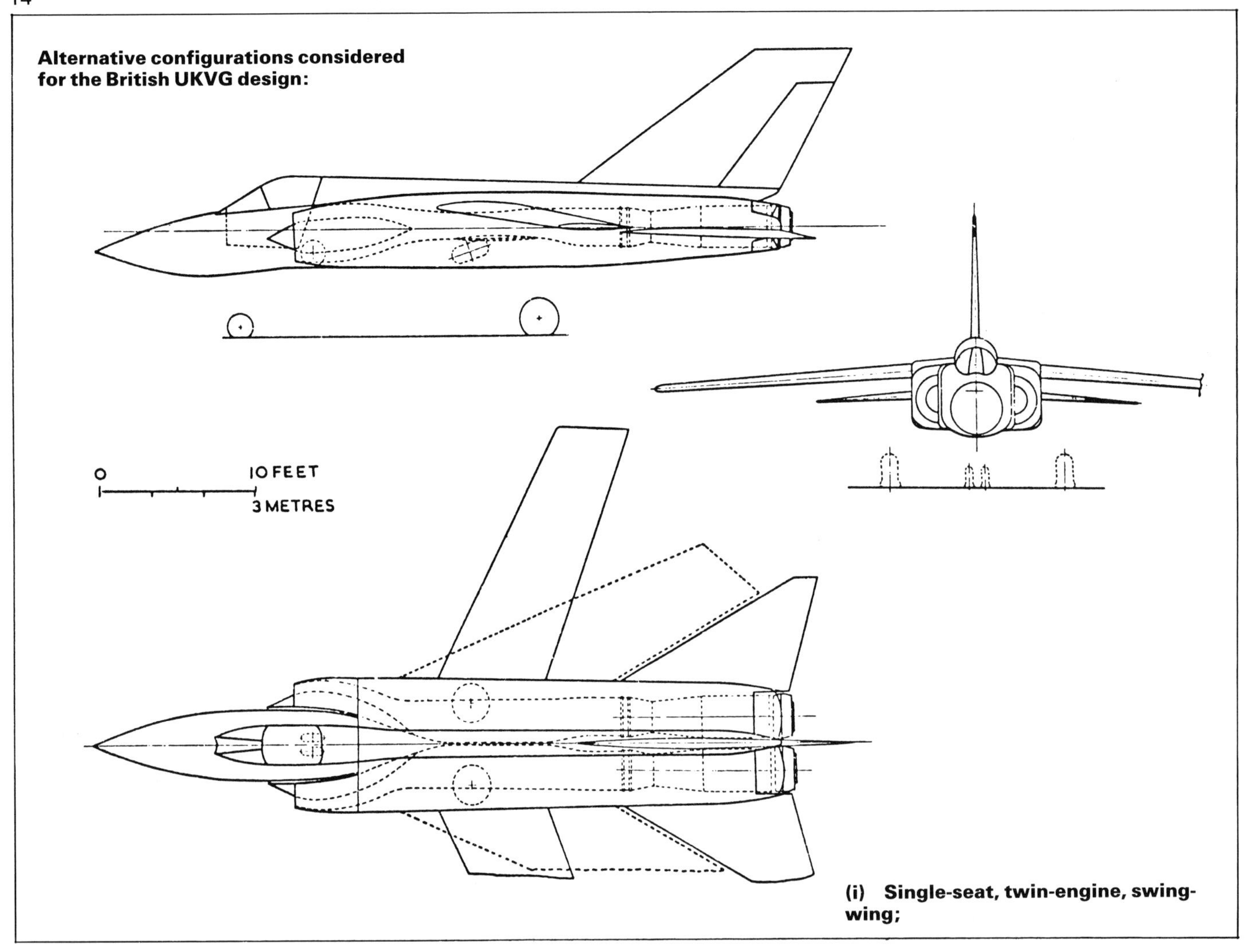

(i) Single-seat, twin-engine, swing-wing;

and so were entitled to lead this programme. But in 1968 the German aircraft industry did not feel sufficiently confident to take charge and, with memories of World War 2 still vivid, the German Government was reluctant to be seen heading such a large international military programme. So the Germans, who had the greatest commitment to the international co-operative ideal, decided on a novel way round the problem. They offered a partnering arrangement in which there would be no lead nation: the new aircraft would be designed and built by the aircraft industries of each of the nations in the consortium and the work would be shared out in proportion to the number of aircraft each nation bought. It meant the Germans gave up some of the rights that would otherwise have been theirs, and the proposal was well received by the other nations.

Since a two-seat version of the MRA-75 had to be built anyway, the RAF requirement for the combat version of its aircraft to carry a crew of two had no major impact on the design. The inclusion of that service's requirements for range and a night and all-weather attack capability were quite different matters however.

Everybody wanted an aircraft to provide air support for their armies in battle but, the RAF argument ran, the best place to do that was not in the battle area itself but some distance beyond it. If they have the choice — and usually they do — tanks and armoured vehicles in contact with enemy forces disperse themselves over quite a large area amongst whatever ground cover is available. Dispersed vehicles make poor targets for air attack. A high speed jet aircraft attacking with bombs or rockets is able to attack only one vehicle at a time, and even if it aims its entire weapon load at that vehicle the chances of destroying it are a good deal less than 100%. It makes little sense to hazard a multi-million pound aircraft to attack a single tank costing one-tenth as much, especially when there is no certainty the attack will be successful. The RAF answer was to deliver most of its attacks in support of the Army; not at enemy troops in the battle area, but to go 40 or 50 or 100 miles beyond it and hit the reinforcements and vehicles carrying forward supplies to sustain the battle. There vehicles are confined to the roads; and if traffic jams can be caused by destroying a bridge in their path, vehicles will bunch together to make a highly lucrative target for interdiction attacks. Against such a target a force of, say, 12 aircraft attacking with cluster bombs and cannon stands a good chance of knocking out 60, 80 or even more vehicles. In any discussion of cost versus effectiveness, the shorter range aircraft restricted to the close air support and shallow interdiction roles always lost to the longer range interdictor. And what clinched the argument was that while the shorter range aircraft could not fly deep interdiction sorties, the long range interdictor was perfectly capable of flying the shorter range missions.

Mounting interdiction missions was one way to support the Army but, the RAF argued, there was another type of mission which the troops were likely to appreciate even more: attacks on enemy airfields, the so-called offensive counter-air mission. The Warsaw Pact maintains a huge fleet of tactical attack aircraft which, if allowed to operate freely, could rain death and devastation on NATO troop positions. *Defensive* counter-air missions by interceptor fighters were one way of hindering such attacks, but a far more effective way was to throttle the enemy air

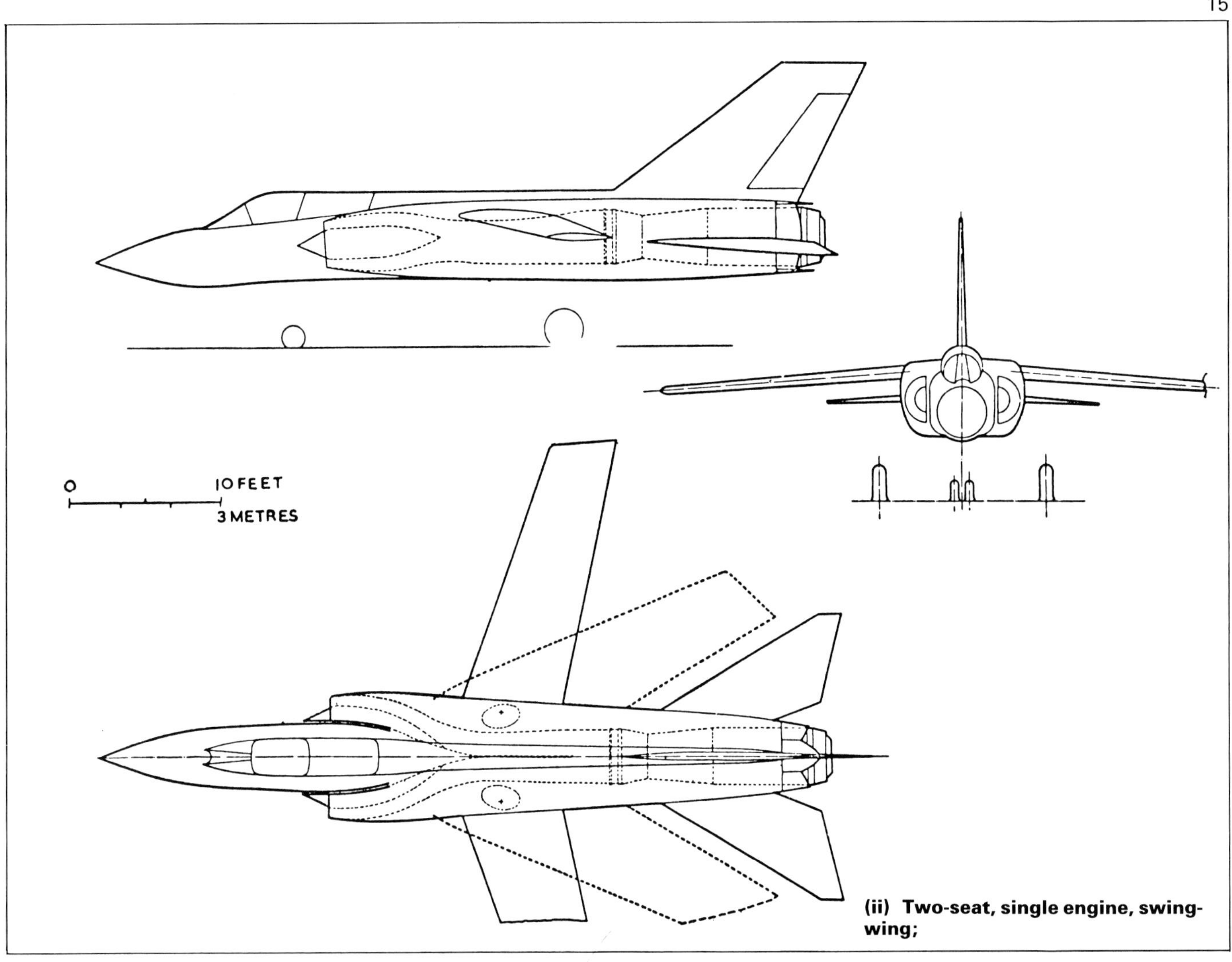

(ii) Two-seat, single engine, swing-wing;

operations at source, by hitting the most important airfields and cratering their runways; if such raids could be repeated at intervals shorter than it took to complete repairs, a large proportion of the enemy attack aircraft could be kept out of the battle. And, to all intents and purposes, the sort of aircraft required for the offensive counter-air role was exactly the same as that required for the interdictor role.

The RAF prepared a similarly detailed case to support its argument that the new aircraft should have the avionic systems necessary to give it a night and all-weather attack capability. Its studies had shown that for operations over Europe, penetrating the air defences to be expected in the 1980s and 1990s, the increase in operational effectiveness resulting from a sophisticated navigation and attack avionic system would fully justify their additional cost and complexity. In the clear skies over the Middle East the Israeli Air Force had shown it was possible to conduct accurate visual attacks using aircraft with relatively simple avionics. Over central Europe conditions are quite different: during the average 24-hour period there is darkness or poor visibility for about half the time in summer and three-quarters of the time in winter; the weather can change rapidly, so that aircraft could encounter a range of different conditions during the flight between their base and the target. There could be long periods when poor weather prevented aircraft with simple attack avionics from operating effectively. If such attack aircraft were committed in marginal weather conditions, formations might penetrate into enemy territory only to find that poor visibility at the target prevented an accurate fast-pass attack. That would leave the attack leader with some invidious choices: to abandon the attack; or press on and make the best attack possible on the first pass — which would usually result in a scattering of bombs over a wide area and little or no damage to the intended target — or the force could continue past the target, turn round, and make a hazardous second-pass attack in the face of alerted gun and missile defences. None of the alternatives was likely to produce a cost-effective attack, and valuable aircraft and pilots would have been risked and perhaps lost, for little military gain.

A large number of cheap and simple aircraft or a smaller number of expensive and complicated aircraft: at first sight the issue is deceptively simple. The RAF argued that what really mattered was not how many attack aircraft could be purchased for a given sum of money, but how many targets those aircraft could attack effectively within a given time or for a given loss rate. Quite apart from being able to attack more accurately, aircraft with effective navigation and attack avionics could cross enemy territory at low altitude at night or in bad weather when they were far less vulnerable to the gun, missile and fighter defences than those restricted to daylight operations. 'The Royal Air Force pressed hard for the night and all-weather attack aircraft and they backed their arguments with actual data', recalled one of the Germans involved in the discussions. 'The other air forces had only opinions.'

When all the requirements from all the air forces were brought together in a single design, the resultant aircraft promised to be a monster. Colonel Rolando Goldoni worked in the procurement branch at the Italian Air Ministry in Rome:

'At that time we in Italy had no experience in designing a modern combat aircraft. Nor did the Belgians,

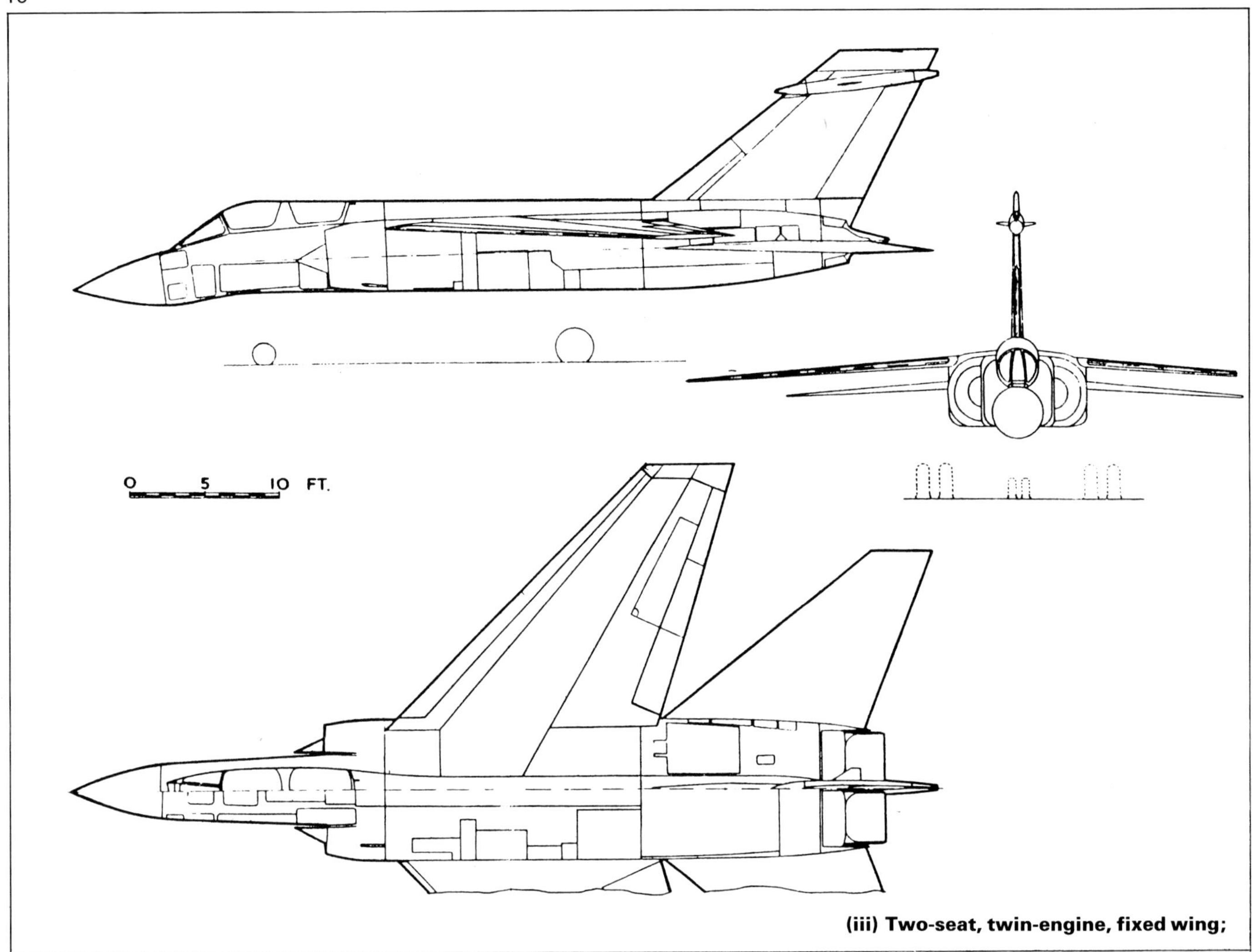

(iii) Two-seat, twin-engine, fixed wing;

the Dutch or the Germans. Initially each air force stuck rigidly to its requirements, with the result that when the first studies were done for an aircraft able to meet all the requirements for performance, radius of action and bomb load, these pointed to an aircraft with a take-off weight of more than 100,000lb [ie more than an F-111].'

Obviously this approach was not going to lead to a workable aircraft, and it was clear that each air force would have to forgo some non-essential requirements if there was to be a successful joint programme.

Throughout the struggle by the air staffs to arrive at a common specification for the F-104 replacement, the position of their nations' aircraft industries was rather like that of unattached young ladies at a ball waiting coyly to be asked to dance, while all the eligible male partners stood at the bar engaging in animated discussion. The industries gave every possible encouragement to get things moving, but they had to wait for the military men to take the initiative.

The aircraft companies were asked to conduct feasibility studies on the aircraft they felt would meet the requirement, for presentation at the meeting of the Joint Working Group held in Munich in the first week of September 1969. Three companies gave presentations: BAC and MBB showed surprisingly similar designs of aircraft weighing about 22,000lb empty, both with variable geometry wings and with fixed wings providing different levels of performance; Canadair showed a somewhat smaller fixed-wing aircraft optimised for the air-to-air fighting role. Peter Liddell of the Advanced Projects department of BAC was one of those present:

'It was an interesting week and, at the end of it, people from all six nations came together for a general discussion. We [BAC] gave a presentation where we drew each air force's requirements as a series of circles, showing the points where the requirements coincided and where they did not. We suggested there were two options. One was to draw a big circle encompassing all the requirements and postulate an aircraft able to do those. The other option was to take the area where the circles overlapped and build an aircraft to fulfil only those requirements. We argued that the latter approach was far more likely to produce a meaningful aeroplane than the former, and postulated a "core" aircraft on which the air forces could add whichever national features they needed.'

The companies had entered the discussions in the belief that they were in a winner-takes-all design competition, but it soon became clear that any aircraft accepted by the various governments would have to have inputs from each nation's aircraft industry.

The September 1968 gathering injected much-needed realism into the deliberations of the Joint Working Group and highlighted the very real differences that existed between the various air forces. The immediate result was that a few weeks after the return of their delegations, the Belgian and Canadian governments decided to withdraw from the project. More positively, the main aircraft companies in the remaining four countries now had a clearer idea of which way the political wind was blowing and began to look for ways to come together. Hans-Joachim Klapperich at MBB was one of those trying to forge a durable link between the companies and he found considerable willingness to make the idea work:

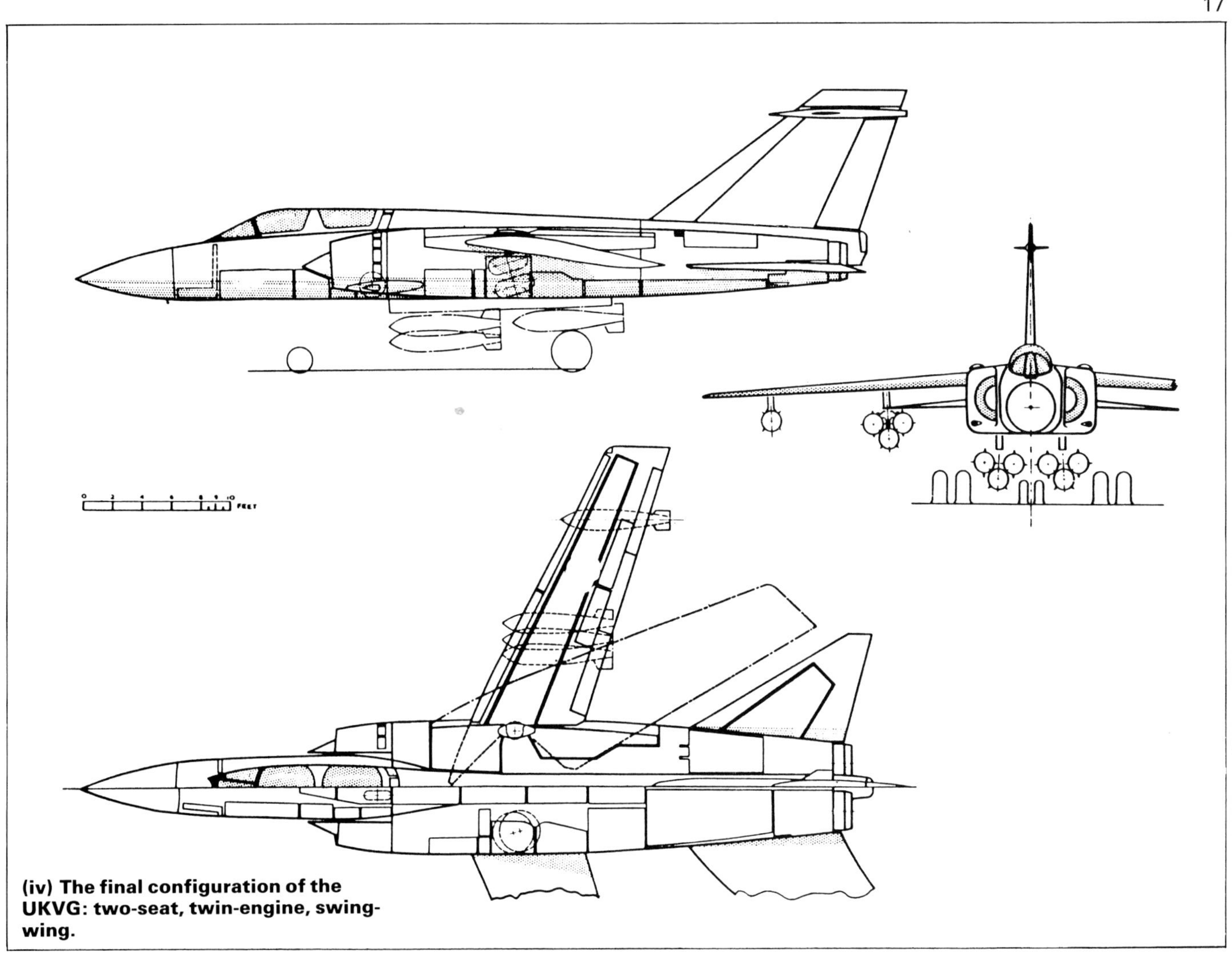

(iv) The final configuration of the UKVG: two-seat, twin-engine, swing-wing.

'In industry there were several top people who had a European vision for the future: at MBB there were Ludwig Boelkow (Managing Director) and Professor Gero Madelung (Division Leader of the Military Aircraft Group); at Fiat there were Professor Gabrielli (Head of Aircraft Division) and Dr Giura (Technical Director); at the British Aircraft Corporation there were Allan Greenwood (Deputy Managing Director) and Sir Frederick Page (Managing Director, Warton Division); and at Fokker-VFW there were Fritz Diepen (Managing Director of Fokker) and Gerrit Klapwijk (Chairman).

'We in Germany had been frustrated in our attempts to design and build an aircraft with the Americans. And the desire to create a German capability to design and build advanced combat aircraft was also a major consideration. We had experience of repairing foreign combat aircraft and building them under licence, now we saw the need for a capability to design such aircraft.'

The BAC and MBB design studies had many similarities and both favoured the use of variable geometry wings, following theoretical work which pointed to this layout being the most efficient for a multi-role aircraft. The idea of an aircraft being able to alter its shape in flight in order to meet the differing requirements for high speed and low speed performance, was by no means new: it had first seen practical application in the 1930s when aircraft appeared with variable pitch propellers and retractable undercarriages and flaps. The variable geometry wing took these ideas one stage further, with a pivoted wing that could have zero or minimum sweep for take-off and landing, rather more sweep for subsonic cruise, more sweep still for high speed manoeuvring, and maximum sweep for high speed dash at low altitude. If the wing shape could be tailored to the different requirements, the wing area need be only about two-thirds that of a fixed wing providing for the same range of capabilities. Working independently, the companies had conducted detailed studies to compare the weights and predicted performances of otherwise similar aircraft with variable geometry wings and fixed geometry wings, to perform the roles of close air support, interdiction and air superiority. Despite the extra weight of the wing-sweep mechanism and the stiffened structure around it, both sets of studies showed that the empty weight of the variable geometry aircraft would be about 5% less than its fixed-wing counterpart. In cruising flight the variable geometry aircraft would consume about 6% less fuel, its maximum speed and endurance would be significantly greater, it would be more manoeuvrable at all altitudes except near its ceiling, and it would be able to operate from shorter runways. The penalties of using variable geometry would be an increase of about 5% in maintenance man-hours and about 9% in the cost of developing the aircraft. On a production run of 500 aircraft it was estimated that the additional complexity of variable geometry systems would add about 1.6% to the cost of each.

There were sound theoretical and aerodynamic reasons for using a variable geometry wing on the new aircraft, yet this feature could have been a structural nightmare. Everything depended on the ability of the wing pivot to carry the savage bending, twisting and shearing forces between each wing and the fuselage. John Waite, the Chief Airworthiness Engineer at BAC, responsible for examining the safety aspects of each aspect of the new aircraft, commented:

'Building an aeroplane is always a compromise. For each discipline there is a counter-discipline which says you have to do it another way. The fundamental one is that if you make an aeroplane very safe and very strong, it will also be very heavy and so will not perform well.

'In a swing-wing aircraft all the forces are transmitted through one point, the pivot, and there have to be enormously stiff structures in the fuselage and the wing to spread out the loads. And that means they are darned heavy. The Americans had a lot of trouble with the F-111 because initially the wing pivot was not strong enough and they did not have a bearing material which allowed the pivot to move under load without generating wear; if there was any wear of the pivot, that could cause wing flutter, with disastrous results.

'At Warton we had developed a wing pivot that would move under load without incurring wear. We used a plastic material, Teflon, coated on the pivot as the bearing surface. Teflon slides well under load, it does not require a large "break out" force to get the wing moving, so there is no wear on the bearing surface. For the AFVG we had built a wing pivot rig. We tried all sorts of different bearing materials and ran the rig for thousands and thousands of hours, continually moving the wing under load, until we got a wing pivot that would work. We were utterly confident that we had produced a wing pivot bearing that would survive on an aircraft.'

Brian Young, then Deputy Chief Aerodynamicist with BAC, was another of those involved in the arguments over variable geometry:

'One of the early parts of the programme was to identify the significant differences in capability between swing-wing and fixed-wing versions of the same aircraft. While we at BAC were wedded to the use of variable geometry and so were the people at MBB, some of the other collaborators were not so certain. The Fokker people were not convinced nor were some of those in the German government organisation. We had to show that the penalties in complexity and structural weight of having a variable geometry wing were more than balanced by the benefits it gave in aerodynamic characteristics in our areas of interest.'

After a few weeks of intensive debate the arguments for variable geometry prevailed and it was agreed that the new aircraft should have this feature. It remained to choose the best features of the competing swing-wing designs: that from BAC for a shoulder-wing aircraft with the wing pivot very far inboard, or that from MBB with the wing mid-way down the fuselage and the pivot much further outboard.

The use of variable geometry was one factor influencing the wing area required for the new aircraft; another was the efficiency of the high lift devices for use at low speeds. Fokker had done a lot of research in this area, which it now made available, and built model wings and tested them in its wind tunnel. The system of leading edge slats and trailing edge flaps ultimately fitted to the new combat aircraft would owe much to this original Dutch work.

On the question of flying controls, the MBB design featured a conventional all-flying tailplane to provide control in pitch, and conventional wing ailerons assisted by differentially operating spoilers to provide control in roll. The BAC design also featured differentially operating spoilers to assist roll control, but dispensed with conventional ailerons and used the 'taileron' system originally developed for the TSR2: this was an all-flying tailplane, both halves of which moved up or down together to provide control in pitch, differentially to provide control in roll, or in a combination of the two if the pilot wanted to control the aircraft simultaneously in both pitch and roll. The BAC scheme had the great advantage that it left the wing trailing edge clear for high-lift flaps along its entire length, and this was chosen for the new aircraft.

Before deciding whether the new aircraft should be powered by one large engine or two small ones, the Joint Working Group made a careful review of the statistics for US jet aircraft lost during the Vietnam War. This evidence showed that, other factors being equal, twin-engined aircraft survived greater amounts of battle damage than single-engined types. Moreover, even during peace-time training, an engine failure on a single-engined aircraft usually resulted in the loss of that aircraft. The companies concluded: that over a long period a fleet of twin-engined aircraft would be more cost-effective in terms of overall initial buy plus operating costs than a fleet of single-engined aircraft having the same offensive capability; that losses in aircrew for a twin-engined fleet would be less than half those for a comparable single-engined fleet; and that a twin-engined aircraft with its associated redundant power systems would be more battle-worthy than any single-engined aircraft. In spite of the higher initial cost, the Working Group agreed that the new aircraft should have two engines.

Two engines, but what sort of engines? Should they be proven engines using older technology? Or should an entirely new type of engine be developed which made use of the latest developments, with all the additional risks that implied? If existing engines had been used they would probably have been American TF-30s as used in the F-111, or Rolls-Royce Speys similar to those which powered the Phantoms bought by Britain. In either case the resultant aircraft would have ended up about as large as the Phantom.

A completely new engine incorporating the latest technological developments promised to be considerably smaller and lighter for a given thrust than anything in existence. During the late 1960s, advances in metallurgy and casting techniques had made possible a major leap in the performance of gas turbine engines. New types of compressor, made from titanium alloys, weighed less than their predecessors and could run at higher rotational speeds to give higher compression ratios. Turbine blades could now be cast in the latest heat-resistant metals, instead of having to be machined to shape, and the castings could include internal ducts to carry cooling air from the base of the blade to its hottest parts. These new turbine blades could withstand external temperatures far higher than those without internal cooling (1,700°C compared with 900°C) which meant that jet engines fitted with them could run far hotter than ever before. Basic physics dictates that the higher the compression ratio and the running temperatures of a jet engine, the higher will be its thrust for a given weight. So an engine incorporating these developments would give a far higher thrust-to-weight ratio than anything previously achieved.

Had the MRA-75 been a national aircraft programme mounted by a single European country, almost certainly there would have been insufficient money available to develop a state-of-the-art engine to power it. A multi-national programme was another matter: the much larger potential production run meant that the programme's budget could withstand the cost of developing a new engine to exploit the latest technological advances. It was decided that the new aircraft would have a pair of new technology engines each developing around 15,000lb thrust with reheat, of a type and make to be decided later.

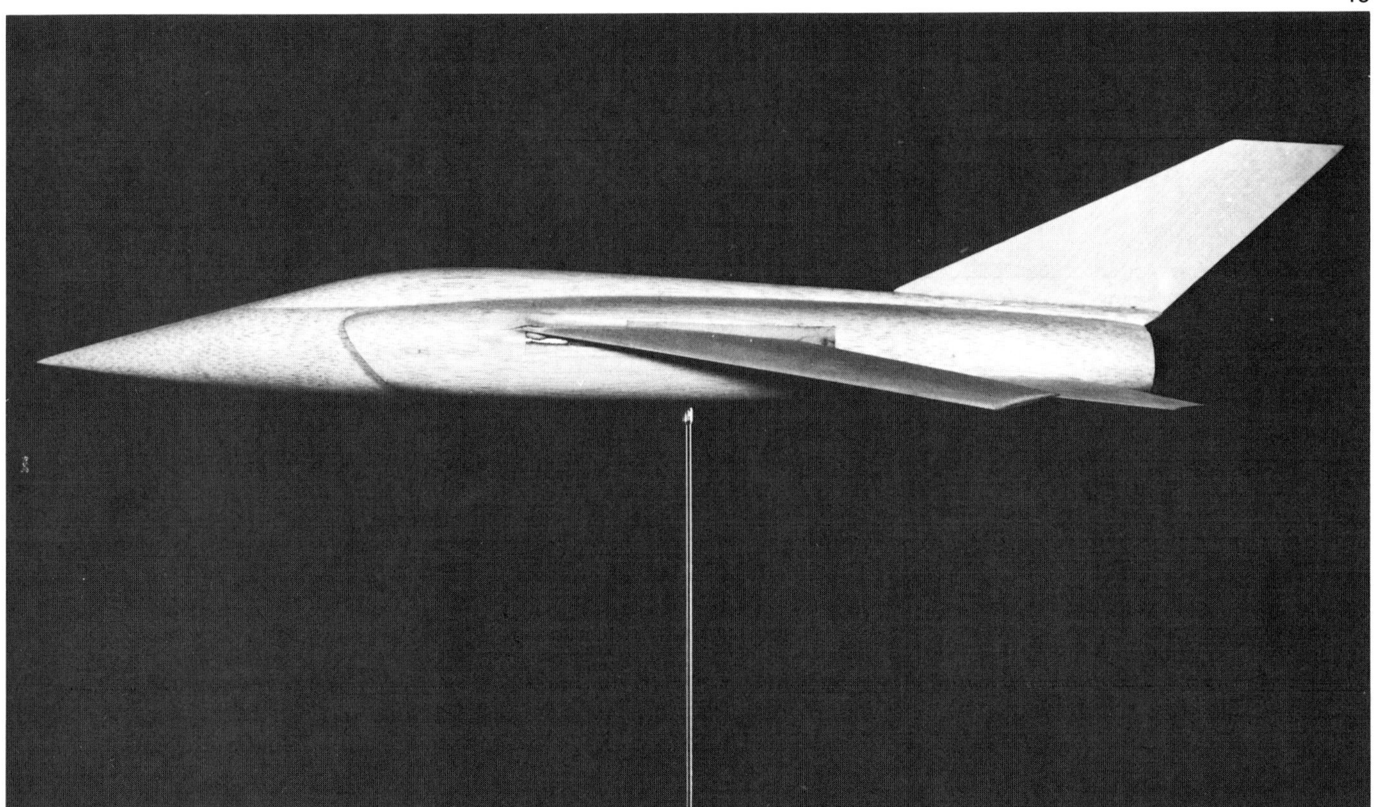

Nearly as important as the number and type of engines fitted to the new aircraft was the type of air intake that would feed them, for on this would depend the optimum operating speed of the aircraft. This potential stumbling block was cleared rapidly, as Brian Young explained:

'The BAC design had a round intake like that fitted to the AFVG. The MBB design had its intakes on top of the fuselage. But neither of those would give good performance at very high angles of incidence, necessary for short landings or high rates of manoeuvre. The Italians were especially keen to have an aeroplane with good performance and manoeuvrability at Mach 2. For an aircraft which has to operate at high angles of incidence it is sensible to have the pressure surface extending forward from the top of the intake, so that as incidence increases the airflow is deflected downwards. The North American Vigilante, a very advanced Mach 2 attack aircraft at that time, had just the intake configuration we were considering. When we discussed the intake, everyone agreed that a Vigilante-type intake would do what we wanted; it was all decided in a few days.'

Along the top of the air duct, behind each intake, there were to be a pair of automatically controlled variable-position ramps to provide optimum flow to the engine throughout the aircraft's speed range.

From the aerodynamic point of view the ideal place for the weapons load would have been in an internal bomb-bay, but there was no room for such a refinement on so small an aircraft. The next best place to put the bombs and other weapons was under the fuselage: stores carried there cause less drag than those under the wings, they do not interfere with the airflow over the tailplane. On a variable geometry aircraft no special mechanism is needed to keep them head-on to the airflow, and if there are any 'hang-ups' the resultant asymmetric forces are much smaller. For all of these reasons a flat underfuselage to carry the main weapon load was adopted for the new aircraft and the main undercarriage legs were arranged to retract upwards and outwards into the vertical sides of the fuselage. Initially the aircraft was to have had only two wing pylons, though later this was increased to four to allow ECM pods to be carried under the outer wing stations.

Above:
An early wind-tunnel model of the MRA-75.

Towards the end of 1968 the links between the national companies were strengthened by the formation of the Joint Industrial Co with headquarters in Munich, to oversee the collaborative work. When the new year dawned, little over four months since the presentation of the BAC and MBB feasibility studies, the four aircraft companies and representatives of their governments' procurement organisation had made considerable progress in deciding the shape and size of MRA-75. The United Kingdom delegation, sensitive to accusations that they were trying to force on the other nations an aircraft larger than necessary for their requirements, kept a low profile during discussions on the size of the various parts of the aircraft, as Peter Liddell remembered:

'At that time the UK delegation was very keen to point out that each aspect of the new aircraft had been sized by somebody else's requirement. That became the firm UK line. For example, the German requirement for short take-off and landing distances decided the size of the wing. And initially the Germans said they wanted all the fuel to be carried in fuselage tanks, with no tanks in the wings where they would be more vulnerable to battle damage. That decided the size of the fuselage. So the UK delegation said the aircraft for the RAF would have fuel in the wings as well as in the fuselage; that would not make the wings any larger but it would give some extra range. And it could then be argued that the German, not the British, fuel requirements had decided the size of the aircraft. Similarly the Italian requirement for a high specific excess power decided thrust requirement and therefore the size of the engines.

'Later we at BAC received a letter from the Ministry of Defence in London asking us to consider the possibility of modifying the aircraft for the role of air defence of the United Kingdom. We were asked to do our utmost to ensure that, however it turned out, the aircraft would lend itself to that role; but we were specifically told not to reveal this intention to the other nations, because it would have been contrary to the UK official line that everybody else's requirements were dictating the size of the aeroplane.'

The United Kingdom delegation were not the only people playing their cards close to the chest at this time, however, for some of the enthusiasm being expressed by Fiat for the MRA-75 programme was mere window-dressing, as Fausto Cereti recalled:

'There were doubts whether the Italian Air Force would be able to afford the new European combat aircraft. So for the first two years Fiat participated in the programme with the main purpose of strengthening its bargaining position in case our Air Force ended up asking us to produce under licence an American aircraft. At Fiat those at the highest level thought that even if the European project came to nothing, it would help the company develop the capability to design and build a modern combat aircraft on its own. Then if the Italian Air Force asked for a new combat aircraft, instead of having to accept whatever terms an American company might choose to offer, we would be in a stronger bargaining position if we could offer an alternative aircraft of our own design.'

Niccolo Machiavelli, the 16th century Florentine diplomat whose name has become synonymous with double-dealing, would have been proud! It should however be stressed that the views held by those at the top of the company did not inhibit the genuine enthusiasm for MRA-75 held by the team of young Italian engineers detailed to work on it.

During the early months of 1969 the remaining points of difference between the BAC and MBB studies were whittled away to make a common design. The last of them disappeared in March, as Gero Madelung recalled:

'The governments had told us they didn't want to enter the Definition Phase of the programme with competing configurations for MRA-75; they wanted us to agree on one configuration. The companies needed the joint aircraft project very much and knew they had to reach a joint solution: BAC and MBB knew very well that if the joint project did not get moving there would be no going home and starting a national project. In March 1969 four of us met in Munich to resolve the problem: Helmut Langfelder from MBB, Olley Heath from BAC, Riccardo Martino from Fiat and myself as chairman. The meeting lasted about two hours and by the end of it we had our common configuration.'

The resultant configuration was clearly recognisable as the aircraft as it is today, with the BAC shoulder-wing and the MBB outboard wing pivot, flat underfuselage, Vigilante-type intakes and a BAC taileron to provide control in both the elevator and the aileron sense and thus leave the wing trailing edge clear for full length Fokker double-slotted flaps. Unladen the new aircraft would weigh about 30,000lb, fully loaded 60,000lb: about the same as the F-4 Phantom and one-third lighter than the F-111. Yet the dimensions of the new aircraft were significantly smaller than those of the Phantom, and with wings fully swept it was little bigger than an F-16 then in the design stage. If it could be made to work — and it was still a big if — the MRA-75 would pack a formidable set of capabilities within a uniquely small airframe.

On 26 March 1969 the co-operative working arrangement between the four aircraft companies was formalised with the launching of Panavia GmbH, a multi-national company with offices in Munich and a staff of 170, to act as a centralised management body for work on the new aircraft. BAC and MBB each had a one-third share in the new company, Fiat and Fokker-VFW each had a one-sixth share. The single-seat version was designated the Panavia 100, the two-seater was the Panavia 200 and both were called the Multi Role Combat Aircraft (usually shortened to MRCA).

In May the four nations signed a Memorandum of Understanding to begin work on the Definition Phase of the new aircraft. However, this boost for the programme was followed by a setback three months later when, in July 1969, the Dutch government decided to withdraw. In that nation, as in Canada and Belgium, the new aircraft had come to be regarded as rather like the proverbial man who was too heavy to do any light work, and too light to do any heavy work. And even in the air forces of those nations remaining there were misgivings concerning some of the things done to keep the programme alive. Heinz Birkenbeil, by then a Colonel responsible for advising the German Chief of Air Staff on the new aircraft, summed up his views of the course of the programme so far:

'Before we went into the programme the German requirement was for a daylight attack aeroplane. All the other European nations and Canada needed a replacement for the F-104, each nation put in its requirement and the requirements were a long way apart. In the second round the United Kingdom came in. They said their requirement was similar to the German requirement — but it was nothing like it! The British required a deep interdiction aircraft with at least twice as much range as the Germans wanted, and all at low level for strike and conventional attack — we had wanted an aeroplane for strike and close air support, with an air superiority capability over the battlefield. But we had not been after an aeroplane for deep interdiction.

'I told our Chief of Air Staff [General Steinhoff] that my department thought the projected aircraft would not fit the German requirement. And then a funny thing happened. The programme was of great political importance to Europe and the politicians stepped in; and military people in the involved countries also began playing in politics. The result of this in Germany was that the Chief of Air Staff simply changed our Air Force's requirement for the new aircraft until eventually it fitted the capabilities of the MRCA! General Steinhoff told me that if our air staff refused to amend its requirements to secure agreement, we might not get a new aeroplane. Originally our primary requirement had been an aircraft for close air support; I saw it move first from close air support to air superiority, then from air superiority to interdiction/strike. Each nation's requirement was gradually changed to the point where all of the Chiefs of the Air Staffs could finally agree. The British agreed to reduce the low level combat radius they needed. They agreed to the short take-off and landing requirements which we [the Germans] wanted. The Germans and the Italians agreed to have an aircraft with a night and all-weather attack capability. And by the time all that was agreed the other air forces had dropped out of the project.'

As yet the new attack aircraft existed only on paper. It did not meet any air force's original requirements; the only people to welcome it enthusiastically were politicians committed to the idea of a united Europe, and the companies in line to receive orders to build the plane and its equipment. Against such a background it is hardly surprising that the project should start to pick up enemies. Ahead of the MRCA lay a stony path, before it became a working combat aircraft with an assured future.

2 The Vision Takes Shape

'If a crow tries to imitate the steps of a stork', one eastern proverb assures us, 'its crotch gets torn in two'. As the MRCA entered its detailed design phase many people thought this European co-operative venture risked over-reaching itself with similarly painful results. Common prudence should have dictated that the world's first tri-national aircraft design and construction programme be centred on a relatively simple machine for one or perhaps two roles and built using proven technology. Instead the three nations had set their sights on a swing-wing, multi-role aircraft, one of the most difficult types to design and build. And it was to be powered by a completely new high-technology engine of a type as yet undecided but which probably existed only on paper. Both the airframe and the engine would have to draw on unproven technology if the small aircraft was to be able to perform the wide range of tasks planned for it. In America the General Dynamics company was having enormous problems with its swing-wing F-111; when this aircraft entered service it was less capable and far more expensive than originally forecast, and it would have to be grounded for the first half of 1970 after a crash following a catastrophic failure of a wing pivot assembly in flight. Was it likely that the European industries, with less experience and fewer resources, could do better with their own swing-wing aircraft? Quite apart from the arguments on whether the MRCA could be made to work, there was the quite separate one of whether it would be militarily useful. As was argued at the time, the aircraft now taking shape did not meet fully the primary requirement originally specified by any air arm due to receive it; the Air Staffs of the respective nations had been forced to accept the machine for reasons of national and international politics and the need to sustain or build up their national aircraft industries. Three air forces, three governments and three major industrial concerns would have to agree on almost every single step of the way ahead, and crucial decisions would have to be taken against a background of three sets of national aspirations and problems, expressed in three different mother tongues. As if all of that was not enough, the management of the international project was to be along lines never before attempted and there was to be no lead nation. There was no shortage of ammunition for the opponents of MRCA and if the programme later collapsed under the weight of the problems it generated for itself, there would be plenty of people ready to step forward and say 'I told you so . . .'.

Following the withdrawal of the Dutch, the three governments remaining in the MRCA programme agreed that Britain and Germany would each pay 44% of the costs and Italy would pay the remaining 12%. Of the work resulting from the programme, Britain and Germany would each get 42.5% and Italy would get the remaining 15%. Soon after its formation Panavia secured agreement for two major decisions which were to form the cornerstones for co-operative work between the multi-national companies: first, that the language for the project would be English; and second, that the three main partner companies would have an equal vote on all major decisions related to the design of the aircraft and all such decisions would be unanimous (in other words, two national companies could not outvote the third).

During their earlier joint programmes with the Americans, the German and Italian companies had little difficulty finding sufficient employees who spoke good English. But for a huge project like MRCA far more would be needed. To meet this requirement the German and Italian companies instituted large-scale language training programmes. The possibility of misunderstandings due to inaccurate translation was (and still is) always present in an international programme of this type, but because the risks were so obvious, people made doubly sure their meaning was understood. Sixteen years later, Gero Madelung would tell the author that he was not aware of a single significant problem in the MRCA programme which could be attributed to inaccurate translation.

The suggestion that each of the three main partner companies should have an equal say in the engineering design of the aircraft, and that all voting had to be unanimous, originated from MBB with the aim of motivating all partners in the project. BAC accepted the idea. At first sight this might seem a recipe for endless bickering and delays, for it gave each national company right of veto over every major engineering decision. But while it certainly prolonged some of the arguments, Dr Giandomenico Cantele of Fiat was one of those who believed that the positive aspects of the decision far outweighed the negative ones:

'Three nations acting as equals in the design of an aircraft: we really welcomed that idea. In previous international projects we Italians had almost always been a minority partner, and it is frustrating when you know your engineering judgement is always being downgraded on that account. We thought it a sound concept for engineers to give their ideas and have them judged on technical merit, rather than the size of the shareholding in the programme held by their company.

'Initially the people from the different countries did not know or trust each other and that caused difficulties. We were all very defensive; people thought the others were following the interests of their companies rather than the project as a whole. But very soon we built up personal relationships and learned to respect each other, and developed a common mentality. From then on the co-operation was wonderful.

'At the end of each meeting we would try to arrive at a so-called consensus decision. If one of the parties dissented from the decision, in practice it usually meant there was something wrong with that particular solution to the problem. If you are presenting an idea and you have carefully prepared your case, if it really is the best solution you can convince other engineers that it is the best.'

The decision to give each national company an equal say in all important matters of engineering design, and to make all votes unanimous, was to have a far-reaching effect on the programme now taking shape. It tended to prevent any one company trying to establish a viewpoint which it then felt it had to defend. Instead, because each major step had to be argued out between engineers who came increasingly to respect the others' capabilities, technical merit was usually the sole criterion for selection. If, for example, there were two competing designs for a part of the fin structure it was not difficult for experienced engineers to calculate which met the strength and stiffness requirements for the lower weight, and agree on the result. Agreement on engineering decisions is far easier to secure than agreement on political decisions, because the former depend on the precise criteria of physics which are the same in all nations. Thoughtful design, tested against careful examination, almost always won out against the gut feelings on which such matters are sometimes decided. Once the structure of the new aircraft had been argued out and defined in quite great detail, the tasks of final design and construction were split between the three national companies. Early on it was decided that MBB would be responsible for the final design and construction of the fuselage, centre, fuselage and wing pivot mechanism; BAC would be responsible for the forward and rear parts of the fuselage and the tail; and Fiat would be responsible for the wings.

One result of this unusual management process was that no individual person was in overall charge of the design of the new aircraft. John Waite, BAC's Chief Project Designer for the programme, felt this was a positive move:

'There wasn't a Chief Designer for this aeroplane and nobody had the right to make his discipline the driving force behind anything. I believe that is why the aeroplane came out as well as it did: it was a team effort, using the best of everybody's ideas. During the project definition stage the structure of the aircraft had been set out in quite a lot of detail. Then we split the thing up and the individual partner companies did detailed designs for the parts they were responsible for within the laid down overall structure. In fact structures were relatively easy to define and to detail. The big problems came with the systems, for example the fuel and electrical systems and where the pipes and wiring should go.'

Throughout the first half of 1969 there was considerable discussion on which type of high technology engine should power the MRCA. Rolls-Royce offered its RB199, a three-spool turbofan then in the design stage. Two American companies were also keen to provide the engine for the new European aircraft. Pratt & Whitney offered a development of its JTF16 demonstrator engine, and also its later and larger JTF22 turbofan (which later became the F100 which powered the F-15 fighter), then also in the design stage. General Electric offered its GE/1/10 design.

In September 1969 the projected Rolls-Royce engine was chosen to power the MRCA and shortly afterwards Rolls-Royce in Britain, Motoren und Turbinen-Union (MTU) in Germany and Fiat in Italy formed their own international umbrella company, Turbo-Union, to build it. Turbo-Union had its headquarters beside the Rolls-Royce works at Bristol, and with some 40 employees it performed the same tasks for the development of the engine as Panavia did for the development of the aircraft.

By any standard the RB199 was an ambitious engine, which would exploit to the full the advantages of the latest technological advances. The design target thrust for the RB199 was 7,800lb in 'cold' power, rising to 15,700lb in full reheat. The thrust-to-weight ratio planned for the RB199 was 7.5 : 1 (that of the General Electric J-79, a 1950s technology engine in roughly the same 15,500lb thrust class which powered the F-104 Starfighter and F-4 Phantom, was 4.5 : 1, or less than two-thirds). The overall length of the RB199, including the reheat, was to be 10ft 7in (the J-79-GE-7 was 17ft 3in), its diameter 2ft 10in (3ft 2in) and it was to weigh 1,980lb (3,625lb). The compression ratio of the three-stage compressor designed for the RB199 was 23 : 1 (that of the J-79 was 8.3 : 1). At cruising speed the target fuel consumption for the RB199 was about 0.63lb of fuel per pound of thrust per hour (that of the J-79 was 0.85lb). And to help meet the short landing run requirement imposed by the German Air force, the RB199 was to be fitted with thrust reversers.

The new engine had been designed specifically for high-speed, low-altitude flight. Under such conditions aircraft were bound to hit birds, some of which would find their way down the engine intakes. One of the design objectives of the RB199 was that a bird strike should not cause an engine to break up catastrophically. Most types of jet engine have a set of fixed inlet guide vanes on the front to straighten the airflow entering the engine, but it is not practical to make these vanes strong enough to withstand the impact from a heavy bird. So the RB199 was designed to run without inlet guide vanes: if a bird went down an air intake it would run straight into the blades of the first-stage compressor, which would act as a high-speed mincing machine to reduce the unfortunate creature to a digestible pulp within a split second. As a result of this the RB199 has had an excellent record of surviving bird strikes; birds have gone down intakes and caused damage on several occasions, but often the engine has been able to continue running; and up to the time of writing, no Tornado has been lost to a bird strike.

The MRCA was a very 'tight' design whose success depended heavily on the engine designers being able to squeeze unprecedented power from the pocket-sized RB199. And time was not on the side of Turbo-Union. There was simply no room in the rear of the aircraft to accommodate a proven engine of larger dimensions even for the initial flight trials. That meant the RB199 had to be flight-cleared by December 1973, the date then being considered for the first flight of the MRCA. Turbo-Union had an unprecedentedly short time, just over four years, to develop the new engine almost from scratch; ideally an engine manufacturer should have six years to develop an advanced engine and overcome its inevitable early teething troubles. Unproven technology combined with rushed development have caused the downfall of many programmes, but they were crosses the RB199 design team would have to bear. Given the way the MRCA programme had developed it is difficult to imagine any way the development of the engine could have been initiated before there was agreement on the sort of aeroplane it was to power. The late start made on RB199 was a fundamental weakness which stemmed from the need to get international agreement to build the MRCA; but had this not been an international programme there would probably have been no new engine anyway.

To maintain as high a degree of commonality as possible between the aircraft built for the different air arms, it was essential to have a single official customer to represent the three national governments' aircraft procurement organisations. In September 1969 the NATO MRCA Development & Production Management Organisation (NAMMO) was formed from senior government and service procurement personnel drawn from the three nations. The executive branch of NAMMO was the NATO MRCA Development & Production Management Agency (NAMMA) with a staff of about 230 civil servants and service personnel from the three nations, split into a Military Factors Division which co-ordinated the military requirements, a Systems Engineering Division, a Legal & Financial Division, a Manufacturing & Quality Assurance Division and an Administrative & Plans Division. NAMMA established its offices in the same building as those of Panavia, thus ensuring close contact between the two organisations.

There are many who feel that of the international structures set up to control aspects of the development of the new aircraft, NAMMA has been among the less effective. It was not that the people in the organisation were not capable, or did not work hard or diligently; it was simply that the framework of restrictions placed on those working for the organisation usually made it difficult to achieve anything without an inordinate delay and an excessive amount of paperwork. The rationale for forming NAMMA had been clear and reasonable enough. If the three nations were to work together on a programme of that size, it could not be managed by independent study groups working in each of the three national ministries of defence. There needed to be a management agency to serve as a unified procurement agency, staffed with the best people each nation could provide.

The MRCA military and technical experts were duly sent to NAMMA and tried to run the programme, but almost from the start they were allowed little latitude to manage because the three national defence ministries simply refused to delegate the necessary powers to the new organisation. As each nation's MRCA experts moved to NAMMA, their places in the national defence ministries were taken by new people with far less knowledge of the project but in whom resided the real power of control. To secure agreement on even the simplest matter, say a minor change to the aircraft or its equipment, NAMMA had to summon these people to meetings at its headquarters in Munich. The resultant meetings were over-frequent, over-large, over-long and usually under-productive. And most were quite unnecessary, because the expertise required to take most of the decisions already resided within NAMMA itself. The final irony was that when the MRCA people at the national ministries eventually learned enough about the programme to warrant the title 'expert', they usually ended up doing a tour at NAMMA — and then had to refer matters back to the people who had replaced them at the national ministries, who were learning about the programme from scratch! Successive general managers of NAMMA wrestled long and hard to alter the system. Everybody agreed it was not working properly, everybody agreed that huge

Below:
The RB199 (above) compared with the J-79 built in the 1950s and in the same 15,000lb class. Note the much shorter reheat on the RB199 and the neat thrust reverser installation (not fitted on the J-79).

amounts of time and money were being wasted in travel to and from the meetings, everybody agreed that NAMMA had the expertise necessary to take most of the decisions on its own account — but when it came to the crunch, none of the national defence ministries was willing to forgo its power to control the minutest parts of the programme. Needless to say, the goings-on at NAMMA were like manna from heaven to the opponents of MRCA and were exploited for all they were worth by the news media.

The multi-national organisations responsible for handling the industrial side of the MRCA programme, Panavia and Turbo-Union, had their failings, but not on a scale approaching those of NAMMA. In these organisations, too, people spent a lot of time travelling to and from meetings at the headquarters and there was duplication of effort. Nevertheless, the pressures on the industrial companies were considerably easier to define than those on the governmental organisations, and their managers could be much more flexible in overcoming organisational problems. The industrial managers knew they had to work effectively with their foreign partners: nothing a company could gain from clever in-fighting was comparable with the unmitigated disaster awaiting all of them if the programme collapsed. High level meetings at Panavia and Turbo-Union were far more effective in securing and implementing decisions than those of NAMMA because — the significant difference — the members of the Panavia and Turbo-Union boards also held important executive posts in their respective national companies. Thus when a member of the Panavia board returned to (say) BAC after a meeting, he in effect took off his Panavia hat, put on his BAC executive hat and then had the clout necessary to implement the decisions previously agreed.

In November 1969 Fiat amalgamated its Aviation Division with the other major Italian aircraft company, Aerfer, to form Aeritalia. The move had no serious impact on the MRCA programme, however.

Above:
A wooden mock-up of the MRCA at Warton, pictured in December 1970. Apart from the shape of the air intake at the lower end of the fin, there would be few changes between this and the first prototype.

Meanwhile, the Royal Air Force's argument that the aircraft should carry the avionics necessary for night and all-weather attacks had prevailed, and from that it naturally followed that a second man was essential if the aircraft was to operate to its full potential. The persuasiveness of the British case was not lost on the Germans and the Italians, but its ramifications went far beyond the design and construction of the aircraft itself: at that time the German and Italian air arms had no fast-jet navigators and if they bought the two-seat combat version of MRCA

they would need to introduce an entirely new aircrew category into their services together with the necessary training courses. In Italy this change would require a new Act of Parliament. The shift was not easy but it was achieved, and in March 1970 the single-seat version of MRCA was dropped, leaving only the two-seat Panavia 200 in the programme.

'If you are building an aircraft that will have a life of about 30 years from its inception until it passes out of service', Gero Madelung commented, 'there is merit in not being too narrow in your requirements.' From the start of the MRCA programme it was clear that the new aircraft would need to remain effective as a front-line combat aircraft well beyond the year 2000. To this end the participating nations agreed that no existing major system was to be incorporated in the aircraft: not only was it to have state-of-the-art engines and airframe, but many of its systems would also take advantage of the latest technology. The aircraft was to have the latest type of computer-assisted flight control system; it would have a newly developed hydraulic system running at far higher pressures than previously; a new type of fast firing cannon would be developed for the aircraft; it would be fitted with self-sealing fuel tanks of a new type; it would have an ultra-modern navigation system making use of the latest techniques in micro-computers; and so on. Each of these items increased the short-term risks to the programme, but once their development problems had been overcome they promised to give the aircraft a far greater capability than one filled with off-the-shelf systems designed a decade or so earlier.

By April 1970 the definition phase of the MRCA was complete. In the previous year the airframe had grown slightly to take account of the additional weight as the equipment requirements became clearer: the wing area was increased by 10% and the fin was made larger. After a careful review of the programme the three governments agreed to begin the development phase and in July the British and German governments, followed later by the Italians, signed a Memorandum of Understanding to that effect. The governments placed contracts, via NAMMA and Panavia, for the construction of 10 prototype MRCA aircraft, with the first scheduled to fly in December 1973.

By the autumn of 1970 the prospective order for the MRCA was considerably smaller than had originally been hoped. With the specification of the new European aircraft now leaning towards an all-weather attack aircraft and away from an air superiority fighter, the German and Italian Air Forces had to look elsewhere for an aircraft to replace the F-104 in the latter role. The German Air Force bought 175 Phantom fighters from America; the Italian Air Force placed an order with Aeritalia for 165 examples of the F-104S, a new version of the F-104 with improved performance and a much better radar and weapons system. These moves, and the earlier withdrawal of Holland, Belgium and Canada from the programme, cut the potential orders for MRCA to 895 aircraft: 310 for the German Air force, 100 for the German Navy, 100 for the Italian Air Force and 385 for the Royal Air Force. Although considerably smaller than at its peak, the tri-national European combat aircraft programme was still substantial by any standards.

In November 1970 the first materials were purchased for the prototypes. Late in 1971, Flt Lt Dick Bogg, a RAF officer seconded to NAMMA, was on a visit to the MBB factory at Augsburg and saw the first metal being machined for the centre box on which the wings would be mounted. 'There was no ceremony', he recalled. 'During my tour I was to see that centre-box slowly being transformed into the first flying prototype.'

It had been a relatively simple matter to share the work of building the MRCA airframe and its engines between the three national companies. Nonetheless, the airframe of a modern combat aircraft is a sophisticated container for a lot of very expensive equipment, and the task of sharing the contracts to manufacture this equipment between the three nations was fraught with problems. Throughout the early 1970s there was a lot of undignified haggling between the procurement organisations of the participating nations, as each one tried to secure the most lucrative contracts for its equipment industry. With huge sums of money at stake it is hardly surprising that there was a powerful lobbying from politicians, air force officers and the companies themselves. NAMMA's task was to take a completely independent line in the interests of the programme as a whole, but that was not easy. Heinz Birkenbeil was General Manager of NAMMA from 1976 to 1983, and he is able to describe the sort of pressures exerted on the organisation throughout its existence:

'We might have four proposals for a certain item of equipment and we would say that out of those four, in the view of NAMMA this is the best one. NAMMA did not decide which nation got the work, it only made the recommendation. The decisions were taken by the nations themselves. We would never say in which firm or in which country the piece of equipment should be built. And there were many times when a company proposed a system, that system was accepted but it was not built by the company or even in the same country.

'All service officers or government officials seconded to NAMMA had to sign a form to say they would not push the interests of their own country, industry or air force, they would push only the interests of the MRCA programme. When service officers joined the organisation, for a time after arrival they would follow their national line of thinking and national approach. How long that lasted depended on the individual. But being forced to work with people from the other two nations, and to listen to their arguments, after a while they came to the NAMMA way of thinking. Although it was staffed by people from three nations there was always a single NAMMA line on any question though sometimes it would be contrary to the British line, the German line or the Italian line, and sometimes it ran counter to all three.

'In following their organisation's independent line, NAMMA people often got into unpleasant situations. For example, a German representative would have senior German Air Force officers coming to him and saying "Why is NAMMA taking the UK line on this matter, even when everybody knows that the solution offered by this German company is better?" I know British and Italian representatives were attacked by their countrymen in the same way. The answer was, always, "We are here to defend the best solution to the problem as NAMMA sees it. We cannot change that!" '

One of the longest-running battles to equip the new aircraft concerned the selection of the attack radar, which involved a series of high-powered meetings between NAMMA and procurement representatives from the three nations. Heinz Birkenbeil describes the bargaining positions adopted by the German and British delegations:

'The German delegation wanted a radar made by the American Autonetics company to go into the aircraft. The British delegation said they wanted a radar made by Ferranti in Britain, which they said would be a better radar. The Germans replied that nothing existed of such a British radar, not even a drawing on a blackboard. In the end, after numerous meetings and discussions extending over a year, a deal was struck. The British said that if it had to be an American radar they did not want the Autonetics radar, they wanted a Texas Instruments radar which was less expensive. And the inertial navigation system, which the Germans had wanted to be made by the American Litton company, should instead be made by Ferranti in Britain. At the end of the day the whole thing was a compromise: "You get this part if you agree to that contract going here and this contract going there." That is a big disadvantage of an international project, there were times when the entire programme nearly fell apart because the nations could not agree.'

Panavia placed a contract with Texas Instruments to build the attack radar in October 1971.

At the three aircraft companies an immense amount of detailed design work for MRCA took place during this period. One particularly important aspect was the harmonisation of the controls and the decision on which basic control forces should be adopted. German and Italian pilots were used to flying American aircraft like the F-104, which had relatively heavy stick forces. Previous fighter-type aircraft designed in Britain had much lighter control forces. After a lot of discussion the three nations' pilots agreed on a compromise, with the control forces slightly heavier than usual for a British aircraft but rather lighter than usual for an American aircraft. Simulators were used to define those areas where the aircraft would be either over-sensitive or over-sluggish, and changes were made to the controls to give a good response throughout the entire flight envelope.

Also at this time, pilots and navigators from each of the air arms and the companies came together each month for the meetings of the Cockpit Committee, to decide on details of the layout of crew positions. Dave Eagles, one of the company pilots involved in the discussions, recalled:

'The cockpit was designed by pilots and navigators of the four air arms, all of which were represented at the meetings. And each company sent a test pilot: Fred Rammenseé from MBB, Pietro Trevisan from Aeritalia and myself from BAC. At first I thought it would be a perfect recipe for disaster: during the early meetings everybody was establishing his position and everybody wanted his say on each item. But things soon settled down and there was a very high standard of debate. It became necessary to marshal facts very carefully beforehand, to get one's point across. I remember we discussed such basics as whether the engine instruments should go on the right or the left of the instrument panel. They ended up on the right where they usually are, but when you had people querying basics of layout it made you consider every single point anew and that was a good thing.

'Throughout the discussions the watchword was "commonality". If one nation's representatives had ideas of making their aircraft non-standard, the others would appeal on the grounds of commonality to get them to fall into line. I remember one particular meeting where we discussed the control unit for the cabin air conditioning. The Royal Air Force and the Luftwaffe had decided to add an additional switch to run an item of crew equipment; the Italian Air Force did not use that item. The proposal was that all the control units be made the same, but those fitted to Italian aircraft would have a blanking plate which would cover the hole cut to take the extra switch fitted to British and German aircraft. The Italian representative, an Air Force major, insisted that his nation's aircraft should have the panel previously agreed, without the extra hole or blanking plate. Various people in turn stood up and, in the interests of commonality, asked him to accept the modified panel. To no avail. The discussion must have been going on for about three-quarters of an hour when a certain RAF officer stood up and said "Look, major, let me put it this way. When God made men and women he gave them both nipples on their chests. Now the men don't actually use theirs, they are there for commonality. In those same interests of commonality, please will you take the same panel as everybody else?" The meeting dissolved into laughter and the Italian major broke into a big smile, threw up his hands in surrender and said "OK, we take the panel with the blanking plate . . .".'

In November 1972, MBB engineers began final assembly of the prototype MRCA, in a curtained-off part of the experimental shop at Ottobrunn. The first part to arrive was the fuselage centre section, followed soon afterwards by the fore and aft fuselage sections and the wings.

While this was happening, the first three prototype RB199 engines were running on the test bench. Engine No 4, the first to be built to flight standards, was fitted in a MRCA starboard engine installation mounted under the fuselage of a Vulcan bomber. Thus mounted, the RB199 was run in the air for the first time in April 1973.

In April 1973 a Memorandum of Understanding was signed for the construction of six pre-series aircraft, built on production jigs, to follow the 10 prototypes.

Slowly the prototype began to take shape at Ottobrunn, but as it did so the climate of opinion in Germany began to turn against the programme. If it went into production the MRCA would devour a substantial proportion of the German Air Force procurement budget and its opponents could think of many better things on which to spend that money. With each week that passed the MRCA's many detractors became more vociferous. The 18-month period now about to begin, from the spring of 1973 to the summer of 1974, would mark the lowest point in the fortunes of the new aircraft.

3 MRCA Gets Off the Ground

As the construction of the prototype MRCA moved ahead, the programme was viewed from several widely differing standpoints in the three participating nations. In Britain there was hurt pride at being forced to co-operate with other nations to build the aircraft rather than to do so alone, and unease that both partner nations chosen had been enemies in the recent past; but after the previous cancellations there was a widespread feeling in the Royal Air Force that the service had no alternative but to take the aircraft, almost regardless of how it turned out. One wag caught the mood of weariness in that service concerning its re-equipment, when he suggested that MRCA really stood for Must Refurbish the Canberra Again! In Italy the air force and industry were both keen to see the MRCA in service, but there were doubts whether the Italian government could afford to buy the aircraft when it was ready to go into production. Yet paradoxically it was in Germany, the nation in the programme with by far the strongest economy and where the aircraft industry and the air staff were keen to get the aircraft in service, that the MRCA ran into its stiffest opposition. Emerging like a multi-headed hydra, a spread of disparate groups made common cause to try to get the programme cancelled. For historical reasons there are many sincere Germans with a deep-seated revulsion against all things military; to them, *any* programme to build a combat aircraft was an immoral waste of public money that could be better spent on other things. Quite separate from the anti-war lobby was a group of people who, for party political reasons, sought to depict the MRCA as an example of over-expensive and muddle-headed military procurement, and use this as a stick to beat the government. Within the military and political establishments there were those who thought that the programme to produce this major military aircraft in Europe could drive a wedge between Germany and the USA, and might become a factor if the latter considered withdrawing its forces from Germany. And there were those who felt the German Air Force should have a new combat aircraft built in Europe, but the MRCA was not the right one and the service would be far better off with something much cheaper along the lines of the NKF.

It was all very well for the three nations' air staffs to lop bits off their operational requirements until these finally fitted the capabilities promised by MRCA, but for obvious reasons this subtle move was not made public and all the original requirements for the new aircraft were still on the table. A Panavia brochure issued at this time stated that the MRCA would be able to carry out the following roles:

1. Interdiction/Strike against land and naval targets
2. Tactical Reconnaissance
3. Interception
4. Training
5. Close Air Support
6. Air Superiority

With hindsight the new aircraft might have come in for a lot less flak if the initials MRCA had stood for Multi Role Combat *Airframe* rather than Multi Role Combat Aircraft. When fitted with or carrying the specialised items of equipment, avionics and weaponry appropriate for each role the MRCA airframe would later show it was able to perform the first five of the tasks extremely well and the sixth, air superiority, moderately well. But the brochure implied that any MRCA could perform all of the roles and that was the view of the aircraft that now took hold.

In Britain, the TV, radio and press would periodically mount attacks on the MRCA as being too complex, too expensive and not the right aircraft for the RAF. These criticisms never reached an intensity where they were likely to put the MRCA programme in any real jeopardy. In Germany it was different. There the denigration of the new aircraft took a far harsher and more strident note and some of the mud began to stick. If a German wants to discredit something he will coin an amusing and suitably undignified term to describe it. MRCA, the aircraft supposedly able to do everything for everybody, was christened *die eierlegende Wollmilchsau*: 'the egg-laying, wool-bearing, milk-giving pig!' Influential parts of the German press began an orchestrated campaign to discredit the MRCA using any truth, half-truth, rumour or gossip that appeared to support their line. For Panavia and the three national companies this was an extremely difficult time. Their public relations departments could only issue statements that the programme was going ahead well but, to repeat a popular expression, 'They would, wouldn't they?' No politician likes to be seen backing a loser, and from the middle of 1971 members of the German government began to distance themselves from MRCA. For the rest of the decade the continuing German involvement in the programme would be

H32

precariously balanced on a knife-edge: one major scandal or perceived scandal, a large cost overrun, an excessive delay for whatever reason or a crash at a critical time in the test programme, any one of these could have resulted in the withdrawal of Germany from the programme.

We shall probably never know the full extent to which American aircraft companies instigated, supported or financed the campaign against MRCA, but they were certainly active in this area and they stood to gain most if the programme miscarried. In the finest traditions of the international arms trade they used all means at their disposal in attempts to abort the potentially troublesome foetus now taking shape. Northrop in particular was still pushing hard to sell its projected P530 fighter and one of its agents, Frank de Francis, made full use of his network of well-placed contacts in Bonn to try to prevent the birth of the new European aircraft. Later he would admit, with remarkable candour, 'I attacked the MRCA with every fibre of my being, knowing that except for two nations [sic] nobody would support it'.

During the assembly of a prototype aircraft, delays in a programme tend to reveal themselves, and the MRCA proved no exception. Many parts and components arrived late, and some had to be returned to their makers for modification before they could be used. Albrecht Herold was the engineer in charge of the team responsible for assembling the prototype aircraft. By and large the aircraft fitted together as its designers had intended though, as always, there were some areas that required a pragmatic approach:

'As on any prototype we had things that could not be fitted together as on the drawings. The secondary power bays, on the port and starboard sides of the fuselage under the trailing edge of the wing, were examples of this. Each one was crowded with equipment: an engine-driven gearbox with a drive shaft connecting it via a clutch to the other engine, a constant speed drive unit, an alternator, a 28Vdc generator, a hydraulic pump. Within those bays there had to be wires, drives, pipes and hoses going all over the place. The layouts of the secondary power bays could not be designed on a drawing board. We built them as mock-ups, had the mock-ups photographed, and the drawings were made from those photographs. That was the only way to do it.'

In November 1973, some three months behind schedule, the prototype was ready to leave Ottobrunn for the airfield at Manching for final assembly and pre-flight checking. For the move the aircraft, its wings swept fully back and nose and fin removed, was lifted on to a low-loader, chained down and covered with a tarpaulin. At midnight on the 12th the prototype left Ottobrunn by road for the 60-mile journey, with a bomb threat to add spice to the proceedings. That was in the days before there was a ring road round Munich and the procession of company and police vehicles had to take a tortuous route through the centre of the city. There were some difficult moments with low bridges, in one case requiring the aircraft's tyres to be deflated to give the final ½in of clearance. Elsewhere branches had to be lopped off trees so the aircraft could get past safely. The difficult journey took six hours and when it was complete there were sighs of relief all round.

On arrival at Manching the prototype was reassembled and the engines fitted, then each of the many systems had to be checked for correct functioning and to ensure that it did not interfere with those around it. Also at this time the new aircraft was painted in a distinctive red and white colour scheme to make it as conspicuous as

Left:
The prototype MRCA seen in an advanced state of construction at Ottobrunn, in October 1973. The three fuselage sections have been joined and the wings have been fitted. Albrecht Herold, responsible for the assembly of the aircraft, is seen on the right of the port-side picture, under the port wingtip, with hands on hips.

Top:
Almost complete apart from its engines, aircraft 01 is pictured at Ottobrunn in February 1973 shortly before partial dismantling before being moved to Manching. During assembly the rudder seal had suffered damage, and the rudder would be one of the last items fitted to the aircraft.

Above:
12 February 1974: nose and fin removed, the airframe of MRCA 01 sits on a low-loader under a tarpaulin at Ottobrunn before starting on the tortuous journey by road to Manching. For good luck, somebody had taped a *Playboy* centre-fold on the front of the airframe.

M.R.C. A
H68

possible during its initial flight tests. The starboard side of the fuselage and upper and lower surfaces of the wings each carried a marking of one of the three nations involved in its manufacture, and on the port side of the nose there was a made-up tri-national marking. Politically the need for such a hotch-potch of markings is understandable, but to many people it merely reinforced the 'all things to all men' image with which the new aircraft was tarred.

Early in 1974 the prototype began engine runs in the 'Hush House' at Manching with the RB199s cleared to a maximum of 14,500lb of thrust — 90% of the design target figure. Almost immediately it was found that the engine's three-spool compressor was prone to surging. Surging can be likened to the stalling of an aircraft wing in that it produces a sudden and drastic reduction in performance: the airflow over the blades breaks away and the compressor ceases to deliver compressed air, with the result that the higher pressure air at the rear of the compressor tries to surge forwards. This causes the compressor to recover but if the original problem remains the process is repeated several times a second, to produce a noise like a machine gun. During surging the engine produces very little thrust and the condition can cause serious damage: the airflow into the combustion chambers falls very rapidly, and before the pilot can throttle back to reduce the supply of fuel the engine temperature might rise so rapidly that turbine blades start to burn away. In the case of the RB199, however, the surging problem was rather like one of those stories where there is the bad news and the good news. The bad news was that the engine was liable to surge. The good news was that when it occurred the engine's electronic automatic control system cut off the supply of fuel so rapidly that there was no damage to the turbine. Nevertheless, the problem of engine surging had to be solved before the RB199 could be cleared for production: quite apart from the almost complete loss of thrust from the affected engine when it occurred, surging reduced engine life.

By May 1974 Karl Knauer, the head of flight testing of the MRCA, was under strong pressure to get the new aircraft into the air. The much publicised target date for the first flight, December 1973, had been passed half a year before and still the aircraft was not ready. He told the author:

'We were under very strong political pressure to get the MRCA into the air, but if anything had gone wrong during an early flight the political situation in Germany was such that our government might have withdrawn from the MRCA programme. It was a very interesting time!

'People said that the MRCA had two engines, so if one failed in the air the aircraft could get down safely. But that was taking an unacceptable risk and I dare not let it fly before I was sure everything was right. Looking back, I now know we could have flown the MRCA while the engines were liable to surge. But at that time I did not know, and neither did anyone else, that the RB199 is completely different from other engines as regards surging. It can surge 10 or 15 times and afterwards there is no performance degradation, no damage to the engine. If we had done such a thing with the J-79 engine in an F-104 it would have been damaged so seriously that it would have to be replaced.'

In attempts to overcome the problem of surging, Turbo-Union engineers fitted the RB199 compressor with re-profiled blades which were set at a different angle to the airflow. During subsequent ground running tests it was found these changes reduced the likelihood of surge to within manageable proportions, provided the engines were carefully handled. Engine running trials were resumed but then a new problem reared its head: the turbine disc of the early engines proved too weak and was liable to shed blades. The first flight had to be further delayed while a stronger turbine disc was designed, built and fitted. It was almost the end of July before the first engines thus modified were delivered to Manching.

While the engine problems were being sorted out, the test pilots were making painstaking preparations for the first flight of the new aircraft when it was finally ready. Since the first prototype had been assembled in Germany and would fly from Manching, the need to share honours between the nations dictated that a British pilot, Paul Millett, should be at the controls during the maiden flight and Nils Meister, the

Far left:
The prototype undergoing final assembly at Manching. The nose, fin, engines and intake were fitted soon after the arrival of the aircraft at the test centre.

Left:
Virtually complete, aircraft 01 is pictured in the fuel flow checking hangar at Manching.

Chief Project Test Pilot at MBB, would be in the rear seat. Afterwards Millett told the author.

'Beforehand we planned that first flight in enormous detail, far more than for any flight I have made before or since. All attention was focused on us, the MRCA was the first really big German postwar military project and national prestige was at stake. They were very worried in case we bent the aircraft during one of the early test flights. After we planned the flight I went through each stage in the simulator. Then I flew the planned mission in a HS125 executive jet; it didn't simulate the MRCA's characteristics very well, but it helped me to see exactly what I should be doing at each stage in the flight of the real aircraft.'

The first two weeks in August were spent in making final preparations of the new aircraft, and ground taxying tests. By midday on the 14th everything was ready for the first flight. Then it was found that the gearbox for the secondary power unit was unserviceable. A new one was flown up from Ottobrunn and installed in the aircraft. Soon after 4pm that afternoon, Karl Knauer, at last assured that the prototype MRCA was finally ready, gave permission for it to fly.

Top left:
With the arrester hook engaged to anchor the aircraft firmly to the ground, the prototype is pictured during engine runs at Manching.

Bottom left:
D-9591 being readied for high speed taxi trials at Manching in the spring of 1974. At this time the RB199 had to be run at high rpm at idling, which meant that during low-speed taxying a continual application of the brakes was necessary. To prevent overheating of the brakes, special air blowers had to be fitted to each main wheel during these trials.

Right:
Work on the prototype, probably during the taxying trials.

Below:
14 August 1974. Paul Millett straps into the prototype before the maiden flight.

Bottom:
Slowly, MCRA 01 taxies out for its first flight.

Paul Millett and Nils Meister boarded the aircraft and strapped in. Millett started the engines and when both had stabilised at idling thrust he closed the canopy and tested the airbrakes, flaps and flying controls. (The test report in the first flight of the aircraft, which was declassified for this book, is reproduced in full in the Appendix at the end.) Then, using his radio callsign 'Luna 23', he made check calls to the control tower and to the TF-104 and G.91 chase aircraft which had just taken off. Satisfied that all was as it should be he called for clearance to taxi, then waved away the chocks. With a burst of power the aircraft began moving forward then almost immediately it lurched to a halt to test the brakes; the process was then repeated for the emergency brake system and to test the operation of the thrust reversers. Then the aircraft taxied slowly to the holding point beside the northern end of the runway, where it halted again for the pre take-off checks. Once these were complete Millett called for clearance to take-off, lined up the aircraft on the runway, reapplied the brakes and pushed forward the throttles for minimum power in reheat. After a further check call to the chase aircraft he pushed forward the throttles to maximum reheat and released the

D-9591

brakes. Its two jet pipes belching tongues of flame, the aircraft thundered down the runway, rapidly gathering speed.

At 140kt Millett lifted the nosewheel off the ground and at 165kt the aircraft took off. For this flight the aircraft weighed about 37,600lb, two-thirds the planned operational take-off weight, and that made it very lively. Millett held the aircraft close to the ground until it reached 200kt, then pulled into a steep climb at full power to maintain this speed and prevent the aircraft exceeding its limits with the undercarriage down. At the same time the aircraft went into a gentle left turn on to its planned south-easterly climb-out heading from Manching. At 3,000ft Millett throttled back to minimum reheat and at 5,000ft he selected maximum dry thrust, reducing the climb angle to maintain 200kt. Later the pilot commented:

'When I took the MRCA on its maiden flight it was just like doing yet another simulated run, everything really did go according to the plan. I kept the aircraft in the take-off configuration, with wheels, flaps and slats down, until we reached 10,000ft. During the climb I tried some gentle control inputs to test response in roll, pitch and yaw to see if there were any odd characteristics; there were none. At 10,000ft I retracted the undercarriage, flaps and slats; again everything worked as predicted.'

Throughout the flight the aircraft's telemetry equipment automatically and continually broadcast information on some 3,000 separate parameters concerning the detailed functioning of the airframe, engines and systems. About 30 of the more important parameters were displayed on monitor screens in the telemetry control room at Manching, where a 12-man team monitored the functioning of the aircraft. Millett continued:

'Every facet of the flight was recorded and telemetered back to the ground. Also Nils and I were using a "hot mike" system, everything we said was transmitted automatically So the people in the telemetry room knew far more about what was happening in the aircraft than I did.

'I tried the engines, moving the throttles to see if they responded as they should. Then I did some gentle manoeuvres, pulling up to 3g; I rolled

Left:
With the Fiat G-91 chase aircraft holding formation on it, the MRCA touches down at Manching after the maiden flight.

the aircraft from side to side, then took it through a full roll. Everything worked perfectly apart from the cabin air conditioning system, which we found disconcertingly noisy.

'Then we prepared for the second most important part of the flight: that of getting the aircraft back on the ground in one piece! First we had a good look at its low speed handling. Still at 10,000ft I slowed down and put the aircraft in the landing configuration with the same amount of flap I had used for take-off — I didn't need full flap because there is a nice long runway at Manching.'

Remaining at 10,000ft the pilot decreased speed to 180kt, then to 160kt, to check low-speed handling. Still there were no problems. Then he selected full reheat and accelerated in steps to 300kt, trying the effectiveness of the controls at each step in speed. At 300kt he throttled back to hold the speed at that figure and pulled a 2g turn in each direction; in the course of these manoeuvres the aircraft reached its maximum speed during the flight, 312kt.

Millett then throttled back to idling power and began his descent to Manching at 260kt, getting the feel of the controls in this configuration.

'We returned to the airfield and made a simulated approach and overshoot. That was straightforward. Then we headed downwind, turned round and landed. During the taxying trials we had had problems with the nosewheel steering when using reverse thrust, it could destabilise the aircraft on the ground; so I had planned to use reverse thrust only gently on the first landing. Once the nosewheel was on the runway I opened up the engines in reverse thrust and the aircraft came smoothly to a halt. The flight has given no real surprises but I would have been extremely surprised if there had been any, we had tested the aircraft so very carefully beforehand.'

Karl Knauer followed the course of the maiden flight from the telemetry control room. He had staked his reputation on the new aircraft being fit to fly, and nobody was more relieved than he when it was safely back on the ground:

'With my team of engineers I had been working on the prototype round the clock, seven days a week, since the beginning of May. At one stage we had scheduled to fly the MRCA in May, so when it finally got off the ground we said the date was the 115th of May! Throughout the flight I stood "with wet hands" behind the engineers in the control room. When the aircraft landed there was a great cheer, then the champagne began to flow. That evening a lot of people got rather drunk . . .'

Below:
Paul Millet, centre, receives a congratulatory bouquet and bottle of champagne after the successful conclusion of the maiden flight. Nils Meister can be seen behind him and to the right, facing the camera.

The initial flight lasted 33 minutes and had revealed no major problems. But such problems had not been sought and a vast amount of work remained to be done to establish whether the new aircraft was capable of the tasks demanded of it. The programme of testing the aircraft thoroughly throughout its entire performance envelope, in each configuration necessary for each of its roles, would occupy MRCA prototype 01 and succeeding aircraft for more than four years after the maiden flight.

It is easy to exaggerate the technical importance of the first flight within an aircraft production programme. In the case of the MRCA it was a political milestone of crucial importance, particularly in Italy where the Christian Democrat government was having second thoughts on whether it could afford to continue with the programme. In its efforts to save the aircraft, Aeritalia obtained support for it from a most unlikely source, as Fausto Cereti recounted:

'The successful first flight was of paramount importance in getting continued Italian parliamentary support for the MRCA programme. And in Italy the support of the Communist Party was crucial in getting the law passed to fund the programme. When we were lobbying for support for the Bill I spoke with senior members of the Party and asked if they would support the MRCA programme. They said they were against all military programmes, on principle. So I asked if the Communist Party preferred to support American industry over Italian industry? I said that if Parliament did not support the European aircraft, the Italian Air Force might be forced to buy another American aircraft. There was a long discussion and in the end they agreed to put their vote behind MRCA. The Communist Party supported the new aircraft for two reasons: one was jobs, the unions were pushing for them; the second was that they saw it as giving Italy a measure of independence from the USA. I am certain that without this support from the Communists in Parliament, the aircraft would never have gone into production in Italy.'

To maintain faith with its members the Italian Communist Party adopted a policy of 'minimum necessary support' for the MRCA in Parliament. Usually this took the form of abstaining in any vote which threatened to terminate the programme, in the certain knowledge that the aircraft's supporters could drum up enough votes from the various other parties to prevent its cancellation.

4 Ironing Out the Bugs

The first flight of the MRCA showed the aircraft could take-off, fly an undemanding profile under the most favourable conditions, and land safely. That was all it proved. As with any new aircraft the prototype and later aircraft would have to go through a lengthy and rigorous test programme to show the MRCA was capable of performing the range of missions specified for it. During this process the test pilots, at no small risk to themselves, would fly the aircraft in a steadily expanding set of conditions to seek out failings whose nature and extent they could only guess. It was an essential process, and one which had to be done thoroughly, if the engineers on the ground were to resolve the aircraft's shortcomings before the aircraft was cleared to go into production and eventual service. As Paul Millett put it: 'If prototypes didn't encounter problems we wouldn't need test pilots, a new aircraft could be put straight into service . . .'

In the weeks following its first flight the prototype went through the more or less standard test procedure for a high speed combat aircraft of its type. During the second flight Paul Millett swept the wings back to 45° and noted there were no unpleasant trim changes: 'Swinging back the wings of the MRCA proved to be a complete non-event', he later commented. During the third flight, on 29 August, Nils Meister took the controls for a sortie to explore handling with the wings swept fully back to 67°; in the course of this flight the aircraft reached a maximum speed of Mach 1.5. By the end of its sixth flight the aircraft had achieved the following:

1 Flight of the clean aircraft within the initial flight envelope.
2 Flight within the initial manoeuvring envelope.
3 The variable sweep wing had been exercised over the full range of settings and been found to incur only insignificant changes in trim.
4 The high lift devices and the airbrakes had been tested in the air.
5 The initial low-speed handling trials had been completed.
6 Handling had proved satisfactory following simulated failures of the aircraft's automatic control and stability augmentation system.
7 Handling had been satisfactory following simulated engine failures.
8 The thrust reversal system had been tested and found satisfactory.

On 30 October 1974 the second prototype made its maiden flight from the BAC airfield at Warton near Blackpool with Paul Millett at the controls and Pietro Trevisan, Aeritalia MRCA Project Pilot, in the rear seat. With two aircraft now in the programme the task of establishing the performance envelope went ahead faster.

When they flew the new aircraft at more than 300kt (indicated) the test pilots encountered a discomforting problem: the nose of the aircraft would bounce up and down vertically. The effect was worse at higher speeds, but it ceased immediately when the aircraft reached the speed of sound. The bouncing was uncomfortable rather than dangerous and did not hold up testing. John Waite, BAC's Chief Project Designer for the MRCA, co-ordinated work on solving the problem:

'We did some pressure measurements around the rear of the aircraft and found the bouncing was due to an oscillating air pressure in the area between the two jet pipes, caused by a breakdown of the airflow above and below the fairings between the two engines. We at BAC knew enough about the back ends of aircraft to realise it was a potential problem, and what the cause was. As an interim solution we fitted a plastic and wood fairing on aircraft 02 to extend the lower part of the fin and spine nearly to the end of the jet pipes. Sure enough, that cured the problem. But to do so we had to build it over the tops of the upper thrust reverse buckets, so until we came up with something better aircraft 02 had to make all its landings without reverse thrust.'

The development and construction of new fairings that allowed thrust reverser operation took several months, and this modification would be incorporated in the first production aircraft and those built subsequently.

Throughout the initial flight trials of the first two prototypes the test pilots had to handle the engines carefully to reduce the risk of surging. Nevertheless, it still occurred from time to time and as more became known about the RB199 and its foibles one salient fact emerged: during static runs and those at low forward speeds, surging happened far more often to the port engine than to the starboard. Martin Steinberger, one of the MTU engineers working on the engine, recalled:

'After trying all sorts of changes to the engine to prevent surging, we finally recognised that one of the fundamental problems lay with the airframe of the MRCA. The RB199 had worked perfectly when flown at low speeds under the Vulcan test bed but, as luck would have it, the air intake tested was that for the starboard side. So there had to be something aerodynamically wrong with the port intake. Turbo-Union and Panavia did extensive model tests and found there were heavy swirls inside the intakes; that on the starboard side was in the direction of rotation of the engine, but that on the port side was in the opposite direction. The swirl on the starboard side caused no problems, but that on the port side worked against the compressor. Once we knew the cause of the problem we fitted a simple metal strake in the intake to straighten the airflow, that cured the swirl and resulting surging.'

Engine intake swirl is not an unusual phenomenon but it rarely produces such problems. The RB199 was sensitive to its effects because the engine had no inlet guide vanes on the front to straighten the airflow entering the engine; these vanes, it will be remembered, had been omitted to enable the engine the more easily to digest any birds which found their way down the air intake.

The other main cause of engine surging occurred if the reheat was switched in, resulting in a back-pressure on the compressor which sometimes triggered the problem. Turbo-Union engineers found that improved control of the fuel supply under given sets of conditions, achieved by altering the computer logic of the electronic engine control units, would overcome this failing. It took a long time to eradicate surging altogether from the RB199, and though its incidence was gradually reduced it would continue to plague the engine almost to the end of the 1970s. Engine surging during air shows became a perpetual source of embarrassment to the Panavia officials, as Farnborough, Paris and Hanover resounded to this novel form of '21-gun salute'.

As the worst of the surging problems were overcome, another failing of the engine was discovered that would be much more difficult to solve. During the early part of the flight test programme the RB199 was not run at more than 90% power. From the beginning of 1975 the aircraft test envelope was steadily expanded and engines were run at thrust levels progressively nearer to the design maximum. Afterwards, post-flight checks revealed with disconcerting frequency that one or more turbine blades were missing. Again it was a story with the bad news and the good news. The bad news was that the blades were breaking off. The good news was that they did so without causing a loss of engine performance or a change in mechanical behaviour, and usually occurred without the crew noticing that anything was amiss. Two separate causes came together to bring

Below:
Aircraft 01 undergoing one of the many engine changes necessary during its early flight trials. In this case the port taileron has been removed, though it is not necessary to take off this component to move the engine.

about this problem, as Martin Steinberger explains:

'We discovered that the internal cooling of the blades was not functioning properly. Sometimes the ducts for the cooling air became blocked. Or blades developed tiny cracks which we could not find using normal testing techniques, and the cooling air leaked through these cracks resulting in local overheating elsewhere on the blades. We had to develop new high powered X-ray testing techniques to find these cracks. The excess heat would kill blades after 50 hours or 100 hours running, which was not all that serious during a flight test programme. But when we ran the engine closer to full power we found there was a vibration problem on top of the temperature problem, a minute internal vibration which the crew could not feel, and that vibration would kill overheated turbine blades within minutes.'

The problem of the turbine blades breaking away caused serious delays in the MRCA test programme and would take many months to resolve. Only after protracted investigations were Turbo-Union engineers able to isolate the cause of the vibration. At full power, savage forces were exerted on the blades of the high pressure turbine: as they rotated at 17,000rpm, their external surfaces white hot, each carried a load of 1½ tons. The investigators found that slight differences in the size of adjacent blades, caused by tolerances in production, sometimes provided gaps which allowed blades to vibrate; if the vibration was accompanied by local overheating due to insufficient internal cooling air, a blade would burn through then break away completely. As is so often the case, once the cause of the problem was known, its cure was relatively easy. Martin Steinberger continued:

'Fortunately, we had already designed a different type of blade with a shroud at the top so that it interlocked with its neighbour, but had not used it initially in the RB199 because it was more expensive to manufacture. When we began fitting shrouded turbine blades to the engine the vibration problem disappeared completely. With improved internal cooling of the blades we solved the overheating problem also, and suddenly we had an engine with a life of 300 hours. Fortunately that happened just as we needed to release the engine for production.'

Almost every new jet engine has had to face similar problems at the beginning of its development life, but in the case of the RB199 these were aggravated by the short development time available before the engine had to power the MRCA. Failures like those of the turbine discs and turbine blades should have been sorted out long before the new aircraft began flying.

Yet another area of difficulty centred on the new type of self-sealing fuel tank fitted to the aircraft. Essentially these worked in the same way as the self-sealing tanks fitted to aircraft in World War 2: the tank was constructed in several layers of flexible material, with one layer in the centre made of an active compound which formed a chemical reaction and swelled if it came into contact with the fuel. If a bullet or shell fragment pierced the tank and fuel started to pour out, the fuel caused the active material to swell until it sealed the hole. That was the theory, but within a tight structure like the fuselage or the fin of the MRCA such a tank could cause far more problems than it was likely to solve. Karl Knauer remembered:

'We had so many annoying problems with the self-sealing fuel tanks that I began to call them self-destroying tanks! If they were not manufactured properly there could be little cracks in the inner layer, which allowed the fuel to come into contact with the activating layer. If the tank was full of fuel and the layer was activated, it would gain volume and if there was no room to spare it could destroy the tank! And a tank change could take a couple of days if it was in a difficult part of the airframe. In the end we had to change to a different type of tank and that solved the problem.'

Right:
One problem encountered during early high speed tests with aircraft 02 was that at speeds above 300kt (indicated) there was a vertical oscillation. To overcome this it was necessary to fit a fairing between the base of the rudder and the top of the jet pipes. Early and late type fairings are shown here. This modification would be incorporated on the production line to the first production and subsequent aircraft.

On 2 April 1975 aircraft 02 came very close to disaster. Paul Millett was at the controls with Dave Eagles in the rear seat. Soon after take-off the oil pressure warning light illuminated for the starboard engine. As a precautionary measure Millett throttled it back to idling power and returned to Warton. Unable to carry out the planned test programme, he made a low altitude fly past of the control tower at 250kt to enable the aircraft's pressure altimeter to be checked against a kinetheodolite. The aircraft had just passed the tower when a seagull went down the port engine intake. There was a loud bang, the engine temperature immediately rose and Millett had to shut it down. He opened up to full power on the starboard engine, but that engine surged immediately, forcing him to throttle back to a lower power setting. By then, the aircraft had slowed down and was dangerously close to the ground, but there was just sufficient thrust to halt the descent and slowly to accelerate to a safe flying speed. Millett took the aircraft round and landed normally.

During 1975 four new aircraft joined the MRCA test programme: 03, the first trainer version, flew from Warton in May; 04, the first to carry the attack radar and navigation avionics, from Manching in September; 05, which would test handling characteristics with external stores, from Caselle in December; and 06, the first to be fitted with the new 27mm Mauser high velocity cannon, from Warton also in December.

With many more aircraft now available, the trials programme of the new aircraft was shared between the three nations as previously agreed. In general terms BAC was responsible for trials related to extending the flight envelope, engine development, stalling and spinning, in-flight refuelling, handling of aircraft carrying various stores, weapon aiming and delivery, and gun firing and bomb dropping; MBB was responsible for handling and performance, avionics development, navigation and communications, terrain following, and reconnaissance systems; Aeritalia was responsible for store release and jettison, handling, firing of some types of missile, reconnaissance systems, and the radio altimeter.

As their part of the handling trials, MBB test pilots flew the aircraft with the

Left:
Aircraft 02 plugged into a drogue from a Victor tanker of No 55 Squadron RAF, during the initial in-flight refuelling trials.

wings in all positions throughout almost the whole of the speed range. Four basic wing settings were chosen as being the optimum: 25° for the lowest speeds; 45°; 58°; and 67° for speeds above 0.9 Mach. These settings were not so critical as had been expected, as 'Fred' Rammenseé explained:

'We found that the range of speeds for which we could use a particular wing setting was very large. For example, with the wing fully forward in the 25° position the aircraft can be flown at 500kt (indicated, 0.8 Mach) without any handling problems. But as one approaches 400kt with the wings in that position the ride is not as comfortable as usual and the pilot becomes aware that the wings ought to go further back. At the other end of the speed range, we landed the aircraft with the wings fully back in the 67° position. In that condition the aircraft comes in fast, its approach speed is 200kt or about the same as during a flapless landing in an F-104 or a Lightning. But we could handle that, there was no great excitement.'

One potentially dangerous hurdle that has to be crossed by each new type of combat aircraft is the series of trials to establish its stalling and spinning characteristics. In the case of the MRCA these were done from Warton in aircraft 02 flown as a single-seater, with Dave Eagles or Paul Millett at the controls. The latter recalled:

'The reason for the spinning tests was that we needed to be able to tell service pilots how to recognise the onset of a spin and how to avoid it. I would not recommend anybody to spin a normal Tornado — the one I spun was fitted out so that we had everything on our side. As well as a spin-recovery parachute it had a special display in the cockpit which showed direction of roll, altitude information and angle of attack.

'The spins began at altitudes around 35,000ft, aiming to pull out at 17,000ft. The aircraft was spun in different weight configurations and with different angles of wing sweep. There was no such thing as a conventional stall in the MRCA: when one reached the point of losing control, the nose would yaw to one side or the other, the nose or a wing would drop and then it would go straight into a spin. The attitude of the aircraft in the spin depended on the position of the wings: the greater the swing sweep, the more oscillatory the spin. With its wings fully back the aircraft would be pitching, rolling and yawing at the same time as it was spinning. That got quite exciting at times, though it did mean it was relatively easy to recover from the spin.

'With the wings fully forward the aircraft tended to get into a very stable flat spin which could wind up into a very fast rotation. If the pilot did nothing it could reach the point where there was so much longitudinal g he could not move his arms and legs, so obviously it was important not to let the spin get to that stage.

'Spin recovery depended on the type of spin. Typically one had to push the stick in the direction of the spin — which is unusual — and the aircraft would come out.'

By the end of 1975 the MRCA prototypes had flown 188 sorties and spent a similar number of hours airborne. The airframe had given few problems throughout and the swing-wing gave least of all. Then, in January 1976, aircraft 05, the first to be assembled in Italy, was seriously damaged during a landing at Caselle. Piero Trevisan had landed a little heavily, the undercarriage collapsed and the aircraft skidded to a halt in a cloud of dust. Ten months later one of the Warton pilots suffered a similar embarrassing incident in aircraft 03 as he applied reverse thrust after landing on a wet runway: the aircraft went completely out of control and slid down the runway going sideways until its undercarriage collapsed and it ended up on the grass. The fault did not lie with the pilots but with the aircraft, as Gero Madelung admitted:

'Everybody had been afraid of the swing wing — and it never gave us any trouble. Everybody considered the landing gear to be fairly conventional, and it gave us one hell of a lot of trouble. With the need to keep the underside of the fuselage clear for the carriage of weapons, we had to ask the landing gear designers for some fairly complex retraction geometry: the main wheels had to fold up and around the armament and into the sides of the fuselage. Basically we had compromised the landing gear in favour of good weapons carriage, and that gave us problems. The problem emerged when the aircraft made its first fairly

Top left:
D-9592, the fourth MRCA built and the second German aircraft, pictured during low speed trials, with tufts fitted to measure the direction of the airflow.

Bottom left:
X-587, prototype 09 and the second Italian aircraft, was employed in trials with various types of weapon and external loads. In this photograph the aircraft is seen carrying the MBB-developed reconnaissance pod under the centre fuselage; this multi-sensor pod contains two 24in focal length Zeiss optical cameras and a Texas Instruments infra-red linescan equipment.

Right:
Once the initial flight trials were complete the first Tornado was given the serial 98+04. Later still this aircraft was camouflaged, as seen here at Manching while undergoing weapon and tank loading trials.

high rate-of-sink landings, but ones which should have been well within the specification of the undercarriage. Two aircraft were badly damaged when their undercarriages collapsed on landing. It was very embarrassing for us engineers: a retractable landing gear was really the technology of the 1930s!'

To prevent a recurrence of the problems the undercarriage mountings were greatly strengthened, the aircraft's control and stability augmentation system was made more sensitive to yaw, the shape of the thrust reverser buckets was altered and each main undercarriage leg was toed-in a little to counter the tendency of the wheels to splay outwards on touch-down. The Warton aircraft was soon repaired and resumed flying; nearly 1½ years would elapse before aircraft 05 could rejoin the test programme.

In this chapter a lot of space has been devoted to the problems encountered by the MRCA during its flight test programme. There are three reasons for this: first, because the detection and solution of such problems are the *raison d'être* of any aircraft's test programme; second, because it is an essential part of the history of the machine; and third, to make the point that although the MRCA did encounter problems during this phase of its development, none was disastrous or particularly dangerous and the catalogue was by no means for an excessive aircraft with so many advanced features. As the test programme progressed it became clear that the MRCA was a remarkably safe aircraft: although two had suffered damage when their undercarriages collapsed on landing, the only injuries were to the crews' sang froid. No aircraft had yet been lost.

In March 1976 the Panavia 200 Multi Role Combat Aircraft was re-named 'Tornado'. Four months later, on 29 July, the three governments signed a Memorandum of Understanding for the purchase of 809 Tornados, including four of the pre-series aircraft under construction which were to be brought up to production standard. Of this total 385 were for the Royal Air Force, 224 for the German Air Force and 100 each for the German Navy and the Italian Air Force. Ministerialdirektor Hans Eberhard signed on behalf of the German government, General Pesce for the Italian government and Air Chief Marshal Sir Douglas Lowe for the British government. By then all nine prototypes had flown (the tenth, it will be remembered, was a static test airframe). As a nice extra touch, while the signing ceremony was in progress, aircraft 01 completed the 500th flight by a Tornado.

On the same day General Obleser, the General Manager of NAMMA, signed an order with Panavia to begin work on the initial production batch of 40 Tornados and took options on a further 765 aircraft. The remaining four aircraft, to bring the total to 809, would be pre-production Tornados then under construction which were to be brought to production standard.

The international agreements stipulated that each national company was not to build all the major components for the aircraft. Instead, to save cost, this work was to be split between the companies as on the prototypes: MBB was to make fuselage centre sections for all the aircraft, BAC was to make all the front and rear fuselages and tails, Aeritalia was to make all the wings. Each company was to run its own final assembly line, however, to complete the aircraft ordered by its national government.

Up till now the development of the Tornado had been, in combat aircraft terms, a relatively inexpensive affair. Had a partner nation wished to withdraw it could have done so without serious penalty. But with each participating nation committing a large slice of its defence procurement budget for several years ahead, there was considerable anxiety about the implications should one nation decide to pull out of the Tornado programme or reduce its order once the production process got into its stride. If, for example, the Italian government later decided to cancel its order, the cost of each aircraft bought for the British and German air arms would be greater. And the Italian aircraft industry might continue to make money out of the programme

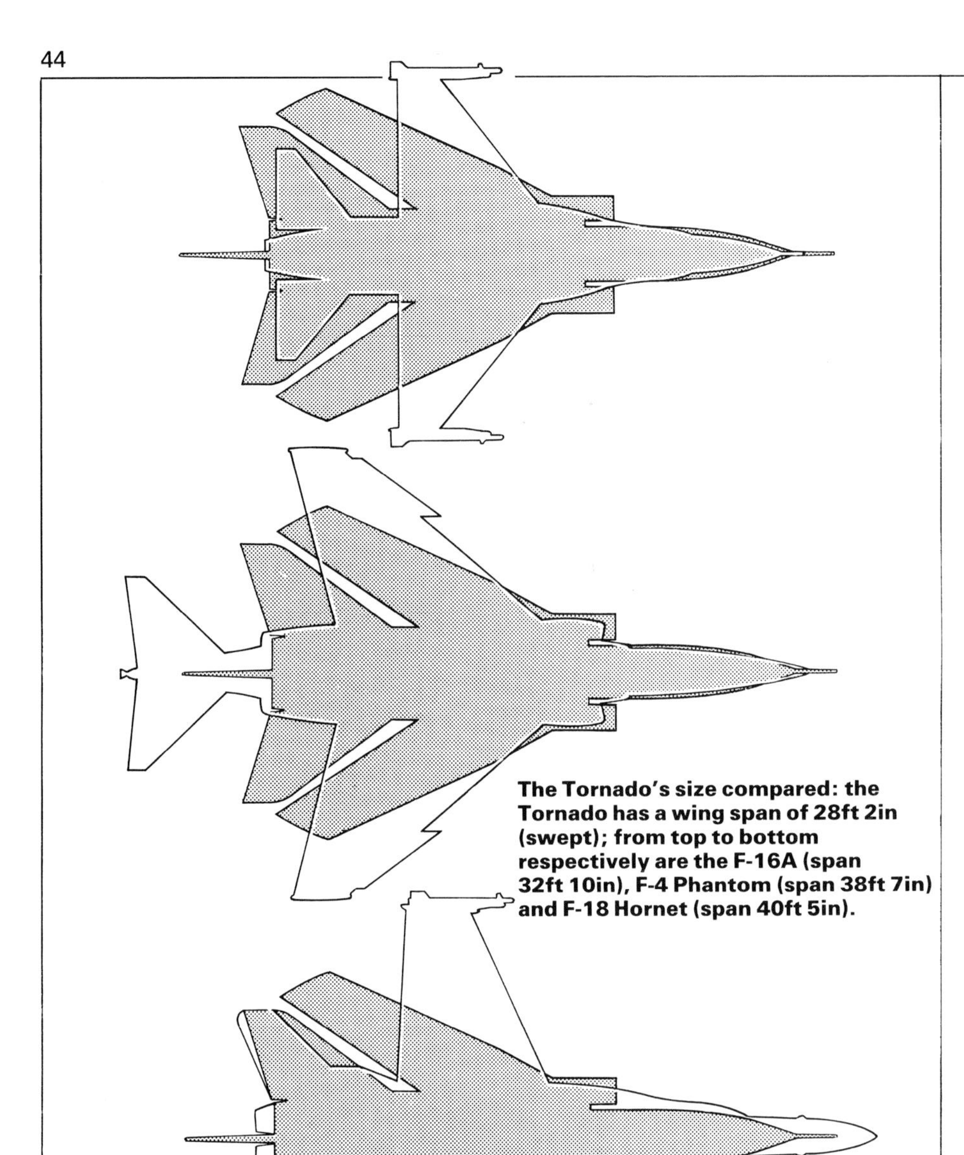

The Tornado's size compared: the Tornado has a wing span of 28ft 2in (swept); from top to bottom respectively are the F-16A (span 32ft 10in), F-4 Phantom (span 38ft 7in) and F-18 Hornet (span 40ft 5in).

unfairly, because the other two nations would still have to buy wings for their aircraft. To reduce the chances of withdrawal and to make this option as unattractive as possible, the three governments accepted tough penalty clauses in their agreement. These stated that if a government unilaterally cancelled all or part of its agreed production order, it had to compensate the other two governments so that the aircraft they bought cost no more than if all those originally agreed were built; and moreover, any government which withdrew completely would have to meet the cost of re-locating the major component assembly lines from its country to the nations remaining in the programme.

Whether or not it was the intention at the time, by accepting these stiff penalty clauses each government in effect committed itself and its successors to remaining in the programme so long as just one of the other partners wished to continue with it. As we shall observe, it would not be long before these terms began to force national defence ministers away from courses of action they might otherwise have wished to pursue.

Below:

Later in its career, aircraft 04, the second German prototype, was repainted in German Navy colours and given the serial number 98+05. It is pictured at Frankfurt between an F-15 and an F-111 of the US Air Force, lined up for inspection by President Carter when he visited Germany in September 1978. The photograph shows well the small size of the European aircraft compared with the American machines.

5 The Air Defence Variant, and Other Problems

Until February 1975 the RAF had kept secret from the German and Italian governments the changes needed to suit the Tornado for the air defence role. Some time previously BAC had conducted a feasibility study and calculated performance figures for a version of the aircraft fitted with an airborne interception radar and carrying four Sparrow or Sky Flash missiles and two Sidewinders, but otherwise with as much as possible in common with the interdictor/strike version. Fitting the new radar, and the Sidewinders on the sides of the underwing pylons as on the IDS version, would be easy enough; but it immediately became clear that mounting four of the much larger Sparrow or Sky Flash missiles, each about 12ft long, was going to be far more difficult. Peter Liddell, one of those at BAC assigned to the project, recalled:

'The Royal Air Force specified that the air defence version should be altered as little as possible from the IDS version, and we started off working to that requirement. The aircraft needed to carry four Sparrow or Sky Flash missiles and from the aerodynamic point of view the best place to carry them was semi-submerged under the fuselage, as on the Phantom; but the Tornado IDS is a smaller aircraft and the fuselage is not long enough to get them all on. We looked at the idea of putting all four missiles under the wings on pylons, or two under the fuselage and two under the wings. But when we worked out the performance of the aircraft in these configurations, early in 1970, we found there was so much drag that we would be struggling to get a performance anywhere near that of the Phantom — the aeroplane the Tornado air defence version was supposed to replace. However, we found that if we could lengthen the fuselage by just over half a metre there would be room to semi-submerge the missiles. But we had to keep the changes necessary for the air defence variant secret from the other two nations, so it was impossible to argue a case for lengthening the aeroplane. We felt we couldn't go to a meeting and propose to the Germans and Italians out of the blue "Er . . . wouldn't it be much better if we made the aeroplane 540mm longer?" '

Obviously one of the RAF's major requirements for the air defence version would have to be dropped: either the need for the airframe to be common with that of the IDS version, or the ability to carry four of the larger missiles, or the requirement for the aircraft to perform better than the Phantom. To Peter Liddell the obvious answer was to make the aircraft longer, but he had to fight hard and long to convince others:

'We were astonished at the difficulty we had in getting that point across; the length increase was treated with the greatest suspicion by the officials. We had a considerable fight to get it accepted, lasting more than three years. We proved that the length increase was cost-effective three or four times over. We looked at various options, but if one got down to essentials it was always a case of comparing the aircraft with the length increase with that without it. The cost of the longer aircraft is not much more but its effectiveness is far greater, by virtue of having semi-submerged missiles and being able to carry more fuel. Put those two together and the effectiveness is very much improved, compared with the aircraft without the length increase and perhaps able to carry only three missiles semi-submerged under the fuselage instead of four. In the end the longer fuselage was accepted, there really was no other way of carrying the missiles and retaining the high performance. They finally agreed on the length increase at the beginning of the definition stage of the air defence variant, in 1974.'

The arguments about the configuration of the air defence variant had taken place behind closed doors and attracted no outside attention. Similarly concealed, at least initially, were the rather more heated discussions on whether this 'converted bomber' could perform effectively in the air-to-air fighting role. Following the announcement of details of the air defence variant, early in 1976, the row came out into the open. Wg Cdr Mike Elsam joined the Operational Requirements 31 Branch of the Ministry of Defence in London in January 1977, where he was responsible for defining the equipment and exact role of the new interceptor. Elsam, an all-weather fighter navigator with considerable experience of Javelin and Phantom operations, was convinced the Tornado could be effective for the air defence of the UK. To him the need for such an interceptor to have long range, complex avionics and a two-man crew were second nature. On the other hand the upper echelons of the RAF fighter community were to a large extent populated by officers who had flown the Hawker Hunter. The Hunter had been a beautiful aircraft to fly (and well-suited to ground attack, too) and many felt the replacement for the Phantom should be a state-of-the-art successor. The Tornado ADV had the full support of the Air Staff, but there was a lot of sniping from those who felt the service was mistaken in taking that line of development:

'In those days, from 1977 on, there was a vociferous group both inside and outside of the Ministry of Defence who were against the Tornado ADV. People had seen the F-16 doing cartwheels at the Farnborough Air Show, carrying a bucketful of fuel and with no tanks or missiles on the wings. We had ex-Hunter people coming up to us and saying "Hey, wasn't that great! That's the sort of aeroplane we want! Can the Tornado ADV do that?" And we said, "No, the ADV can't, it is a long range interceptor not a dog-fighter." The ex-Hunter pilots went around saying things like "The Tornado ADV? It's rubbish! Couldn't fight its way out of a soggy paper bag!"

'Don't get me wrong. The F-16 is a terrific performer — the best dogfighter in the business in my view. But it is single-engined, single-seat. It carries smart avionics but not much of it. It is the right aeroplane for a dogfight in the middle of Europe, but it is not the right aeroplane for the air defence of the United Kingdom and ships far out to sea . . .

'You have to put the Tornado ADV into context. Our "worst case" operational scenario is a fighting area 400 miles out to sea on a dark and dirty night, with lots of targets at low level and heavy ECM. There could be all sorts of other things happening: airborne warning aircraft and tankers in the area, fuel states to worry about, radar warning receiver signals coming in perhaps from enemy and friendly aircraft and enemy and friendly ships, data link information flashing around all over the place, and the crew needing to keep track of their exact position the whole time to avoid flying into "friendly" missile engagement zones. We need an aircraft which, in extremis, can operate autonomously and intercept enemy aircraft under those conditions. I believed, and I still believe, it is too big a task for one man to perform effectively. Obviously there will come a time when computers get to the point where they enable one man to cope with that task quite well. But we are not there yet.'

Had the case to abandon the air defence variant readily been pressed, and the British government supported it, this would have had a major impact on the Tornado programme as a whole. The total British requirement for 385 Tornados included 165 interceptors. So if the ADV had been cancelled and no other customer could be found to take

that number of IDS aircraft, the total order for the RAF would have been reduced to 220 aircraft, the unit cost of the remaining Tornados would have increased and the British government would have had to pay compensation to the other two nations.

That was one major argument for sticking with the Tornado ADV and making the best of it. Equally important, from the RAF's point of view, was the question of which aircraft type could perform the required task more efficiently for the same or a lower price. The government stood by its decision not to order a major new combat aircraft built only in Britain, and in any case the RAF order was too small to justify such a course. So if another type was ordered for the air defence role it would have to be a foreign design. At the end of 1977 the Operational Requirements Branch was told to examine all possible replacement aircraft, as Mike Elsam remembered:

'As a result of cost-overruns the Tornado ADV was beginning to look a very expensive aeroplane and people began to ask us to justify it. Almost every time a new politician became involved in defence matters, or a new RAF officer moved into a senior post at the MoD, he would say "Surely there must be something else we can buy that will do the job better and cheaper than the ADV?" I was told to look at the possibilities, with the proviso that any alternative to the Tornado ADV had either to be able to meet the operational requirement for less cost, or demonstrate a significant improvement in operational capability for the same cost.

'Against that background we could rule out all those aircraft which did not meet the RAF operational requirement for a fighter with a crew of two and a very good avionic capability. An aeroplane with a relatively low avionic capability would not meet the requirement, so out went the F-16. That also ruled out the French fighters, the

Left:
BT001 and GT001, respectively the first British trainer and the first German trainer, underwent their roll-out ceremonies within a day of each other at Warton and Manching in June 1979.

Below:
German trainer 002 pictured during its first flight, in March 1980. At this time Tornados were usually left in primer paint during factory test flying, and were camouflaged immediately before delivery. Later this practice was changed, and it became usual for Tornados to make their initial test flights in service livery.

Bottom:
A Batch 1 Tornado IDS aircraft for the Royal Air Force nearing completion in the assembly hall at Warton.

Mirage F1 and the Mirage 2000; they did not carry the sort of avionics we wanted and the French missiles were not a patch on those the RAF was using; it also ruled out the Swedish Viggen. The F-18 looked moderately attractive, but there was no two-seat fighter version and we were firmly tied to a two-seater. To modify the F-18 into a two-seat fighter would have pushed up its cost, and already it was more expensive than the projected cost of the Tornado ADV.

'The F-14 has a greater capability than the Tornado ADV, but it costs half as much again. At the time we did the comparison with the F-14 the US Navy was having appalling problems with reliability and maintainability and we would not have bought it on that score alone. On those counts the F-14 never even got in the shuffle.

'In the end the only alternative we could consider seriously was a two-seat version of the F-15. The F-15 has the weapons carrying capability we want and there is no question its avionics systems could have been modified for our purpose and we could have put in two seats. It could have been a viable political option, also. In the summer of 1979 there was a sniff of interest in the Tornado from the USAF. They were looking for an attack aircraft to fill the gap between the F-111 and the F-16, they wanted about 150 aeroplanes which could have been Tornados. They might have been offered the Tornado IDS, and had they bought it the British government would cancel the ADV and then buy 165 two-seat F-15s instead. But the USAF interest in the Tornado fell away and the idea never got off the ground.

'The two-seat F-15 would have done most of the things we want. It is a great aeroplane, the pilots love it, it is excellent in a medium altitude or high altitude fight. But take it below 5,000ft at high speed on a bumpy day and boy, have you got problems. That big wing doesn't like being down there, it is all lift. That is the big difference between it and the Tornado.'

And the two-seat F-15 with upgraded avionics would certainly not have been any cheaper than the Tornado ADV. Whichever way the OR Branch looked at the problem, the Tornado seemed to come out as the most effective aircraft available for the specialised UK air defence role, at the price.

The RAF was not the only organisation with mixed views on the Tornado at this time. In 1976 General Heinz Birkenbeil became head of NAMMA, and over the next four years he observed the almost continual attacks by those who wished the German government to pull out of the Tornado programme.

'At that time the Tornado programme was always in the balance. The project was divided into phases of development lasting a year, separated by check points. At each check point there would be several meetings to decide whether or not to continue with the programme, and some of the check points took months to resolve. In Germany there was always a big fight, whether or not to continue with Tornado. But there really was no alternative aircraft type available which could have done its job.'

In spring of 1980, German politicians initiated what was to be the final attempt to terminate their nation's part in the Tornado programme following an apparent major cost-overrun (a detailed governmental investigation later established that this had not been the case; the higher cost of the aircraft was due almost entirely to inflation and the increased price of raw materials, notably titanium). The new Social Democratic government ordered the Ministry of Defence in Bonn to conduct a secret investigation of the implications of pulling out of the Tornado programme. It immediately became clear that the penalties of doing so would have been substantially greater than those facing the British government had it cancelled only the air defence variant, as Heinz Birkenbeil explained:

'By then material had been ordered for 809 aircraft; if Germany cancelled its 324 aircraft the price of each of the remaining 485 Tornados for the other two nations would have increased tremendously. The German government would have had to subsidise these aircraft so that they cost the same as before. Also, the German government would have had to foot the bill for moving the production lines making major assemblies and relocating them in the other two countries, leaving idle the German factories which had been making those assemblies. Taken together, those things would have cost almost as much as remaining in the programme and the German Air Force and Navy would have had no aeroplanes to show for the huge amount of money spent.'

It was clear to the German government that the only avenue of escape from the Tornado programme ran straight through the middle of a political minefield, and the withdrawal proposal was quietly forgotten. The programme had now developed so powerful a momentum that it was virtually impossible for any single government to pull out, no matter how much it wanted to.

While the politicians and military men had been arguing on the merits of continuing with part or all of the Tornado programme, the processes of production and testing had accelerated steadily. Several more Tornados joined the test programme. In March 1976, aircraft 07 flew from Manching fitted with a fully integrated avionics system; in July aircraft 08 flew from Warton, to be used for weapons trials. In February 1977 there were two new aircraft: 09, from Caselle, destined for weapons trials; and 11, from Manching, the first pre-production series aircraft, which would be used for stores handling and tests of the electronic countermeasures systems. (Aircraft 10 was a static test aircraft at Warton.) Aircraft 12 flew from Warton in March; it would be used for trials of the weapon aiming and ECM systems. Shortly afterwards aircraft 02, used to explore the high speed end of the performance envelope, exceeded Mach 1.9 in level flight at high altitude. In June 1977 the total number of hours flown by all Tornados reached 1,000. Aircraft 13, flew from Manching in January 1978 and would be used in trials of the automatic terrain following system and carrying various types of store. It was followed in March by aircraft 15 from Warton with a production rear fuselage, taileron and fin. Aircraft 14, the first with production wings, flew from Caselle in January 1979, followed in March by Aircraft 16 from Manching with a production forward fuselage.

Remarkably, for a combat aircraft designed for the hazardous low altitude attack role and now starting to amass a large number of flying hours, for nearly five years since the first flight there had been no aircrew fatalities and no Tornados had been lost. Then, on 12 June 1979, tragedy struck. During a simulated toss bombing manoeuvre, aircraft 08 flying from Warton crashed into the Irish Sea killing Russ Pengelly and Sqn Ldr John Gray. In April 1980 aircraft 04, flying from Manching, crashed while practising a display routine for the Hannover Air Show, killing Ludwig Obermeier and Kurt Schreiber from MBB. Both accidents were thoroughly investigated, and there was clear evidence there had been no failure of the aircraft or its systems in either case.

By December 1980, 12 prototypes (including three air defence variants), six pre-production and 25 production Tornados (IDS trainers and combat aircraft) had flown. The remaining 15 aircraft in the first production batch were all undergoing final assembly, as were the first 20 of the 110 aircraft in the second batch, and aircraft were coming off the assembly lines at Warton and Manching at a rate of about 10 per month. Work was well advanced on the manufacture of components and major assemblies for the 164 aircraft in the third production batch.

The scale of the Tornado programme was now huge. Nine companies with 15 plants scattered throughout the three nations were building or assembling airframe components; 11 factories were making the engines and associated systems; and some 500 smaller companies were also taking part in the programme. In all, more than 70,000 workers were involved in building Tornados. Components converged by road on the assembly plants at Warton, Manching and Caselle, in many cases after a detour through France because the Swiss and Austrian neutrality laws prohibit the passage of foreign military materiel through their territory.

At the close of 1980, just over 13 years since the initial discussions to build an aircraft to replace the F-104, the Tornado had 4,800 flying hours behind it and was on the point of entering service. Now it would be discovered whether the immense amount of effort and money put into the programme had really been worthwhile, or if the three nations' aircraft industries had overreached themselves to a disastrous extent.

Panavia Tornado

Left:
A pair of Tornados of Marinefliegergeschwader 1 of the German Navy make a spectacular shot as they break formation over the Baltic. Pictured shortly after the unit re-equipped, the aircraft carry the colour scheme applied initially.

D-9591
MRCA
D-9591

Top left:
Prototype D-9591 pictured during high-thrust engine runs at Manching, shortly before its maiden flight.

Left:
After painting, prototype Tornado D-9591 was moved into the 'hush house' at Manching in the spring of 1974 for its initial engine running trials. Still the aircraft lacked its rudder, though this would be fitted shortly afterwards.

Top:
The pilot's cockpit of the IDS version, with the ejector seat removed.

Above:
A close-up of the pilot's instrument panel, showing the moving-map display in operation.

Above:
ZA458 'FB' heads a No 16 Squadron line-up. *Peter R. Foster*

Below:
A GR1 of No 31 Squadron.
Flt Lt T. R. Paxton

Above:
Tornado GR1 ZA599 of No 9 Squadron, the flaps and slats in the landing configuration. *Peter R. Foster*

Below:
A Tornado of No 27 Squadron undergoing maintenance on the flight line at Nellis AFB, Nevada, during one of the 'Green Flag' exercises in 1983.
Frank Mormillo

Bottom:
An aircraft of No 617 Squadron on the flight line at Nellis, with two practice bomb containers under the fuselage.
Frank Mormillo

G-20
G-75
G-70
43 12

Right:
German Tornado G-38, a training version operated by the TTTE, showing the camouflage scheme applied initially to Luftwaffe aircraft. *Flt Lt T. R. Paxton*

Below right:
Tornados of Jagdbombergeschwader 32 based at Lechfeld in southern Germany, wearing the later three-tone camouflage scheme applied to Luftwaffe attack aircraft.

Bottom left:
A line-up of Tornados, mainly German, of the Tri-National Tornado Training Unit on the flight line at Cottesmore in April 1982. *Peter R. March*

Below:
Tornado 44+10 of JaboG 38 is seen here with thrust reversers engaged and wing flaps configured for landing.

Right:
A Tornado of the 155° Gruppo of the 6° Stormo, based at Bari in the south of Italy. The aircraft carries four 330 Imp gal (1,500-litre) tanks, and is shown in the maximum-range configuration employed during radar reconnaissance missions. *Herman Sixma*

Bottom left:
Another Tornado of 155° Gruppo, 6° Stormo, fitted with a pair of Kormoran missiles and configured for the anti-shipping role. *Herman Sixma*

Bottom right:
An aircraft in the markings of the 154° Gruppo of the 6° Stormo, the 'Red Devils', based at Ghedi. *Herman Sixma*

SALVATAGGIO
RESCUE
NOTFALL
36
41

TORNADO
6
11

Far left:
No place for a failure . . . Tornados of No 9 Squadron taking fuel from a Victor tanker of No 57 Squadron south of Greenland, during the return from their first detachment to Goose Bay in Labrador early in 1983. The nearer aircraft was venting fuel from the fin tank, but the amount lost was not large and it was able to complete the flight.
Flt Lt T. R. Paxton

Below left:
A Tornado F3 of No 29 Squadron with its flight refuelling probe in the extended position. On this version the probe is mounted on the port side of the fuselage; on the IDS version it is on the starboard side. *Flt Lt T. R. Paxton*

Left:
A close-up of ZE209 of No 29 Squadron taking fuel from the starboard hose of a VC10 tanker of No 101 Squadron.
Peter R. Foster

Below:
This fine shot shows an F2 of No 229 OCU refuelling from a VC10, while another holds off to one side.
Flt Lt R. Burden

Bottom:
A Tornado navigator's-eye view of a VC10, during a refuelling operation over the North Sea. *Flt Lt R. Burden*

Right:

GR1 ZA449 in formation with F2T ZD899. The lighter colouring of the ADV makes it look even longer than the IDS version than is in fact the case.

Below:

ZE288 of No 29 Squadron, the first RAF front-line fighter unit to become operational with Tornados. Note the squadron's badge on the tail, and its distinctive triple-X marking along the air intake. The wing slats and flaps are shown in the landing position.
Flt Lt T. R. Paxton

Left:
A Tornado F3 of No 229 OCU with flaps and slats in the manoeuvring position, trailing vortices from the wingtips as it pulls a high-G turn on a damp day. *Peter R. March*

Right:
Tornado F3 ZE156 'AM' of No 229 OCU pictured in the spring of 1987, bearing the unit's marking on the tail and that of No 65 Squadron (the unit designation it would adopt in time of war) in front of the air intake. *R. L. Ward*

Left and below left:
During the design of the Tornado high priority was given to ease of maintenance and accessibility of systems. Shown here are the access to the starboard taileron hydraulic jack and to the cockpit instruments.

Bottom:
A busy scene at the Waffenausbildungskomponente (WaKo), the weapons training unit at Erding which was first in the Luftwaffe to receive Tornados.

Right:
Tornados of the Royal Saudi Arabian Air Force, delivered from an IDS batch originally ordered for the RAF, showing the distinctive desert camouflage scheme applied to these aircraft.

Below right:
A pair of Tornados of No 31 Squadron, based at Brüggen in Germany, showing the wrap-around camouflage scheme and one of the standard weapons loads carried — four 1,000lb bombs, two drop tanks, a BOZ chaff/flare dispenser under the starboard wing and a Sky Shadow jamming pod under the port wing.
Flt Lt T. R. Paxton

704
701
ROYAL SAUDI AIR FORCE

ZD844
ZD844

Above:
Tornado operations by night.

6 The Tornado IDS Described

With the Tornado well established in production, let us take a detailed look at the attack version of the aircraft being delivered to the three nations' air services from 1981; in its essentials this is the same aircraft as that being delivered at the time of writing.

The interdictor/strike version of the Tornado (the air defence variant will be described in a later chapter) has been optimised for air-to-surface attack which includes the offensive counter-air, battlefield interdiction, close air support and anti-shipping roles.

The aircraft's maximum take-off weight is just over 60,000lb, but that is a not-to-be exceeded figure and in the operational configuration the aircraft would normally take-off at rather less than that. The empty equipped weight of the aircraft is just over 31,000lb, divided between structure (about 16,000lb), engines and associated systems (about 6,600lb) and equipment (about 8,400lb). A typical operational load for a Tornado IDS is up to 9,000lb of bombs or other weapons under the fuselage, and two 332 Imp gal (1,500-litre) fuel tanks, two ECM pods and two Sidewinder missiles on the wing pylons.

When 'clean' the Tornado is capable of supersonic speed at all altitudes, but carrying an operational load its maximum speed at low level is about 600kt.

The fuselage is a conventional aluminium alloy structure with integrally stiffened skin, apart from the central box carrying the wing pivots which is made from titanium alloy. The interior of the fuselage is divided, by volume, into three roughly equal parts: one third for the engines, one third for fuel, and one-third for the crew, flying controls and avionics. The aircraft can be fitted with a retractable flight refuelling probe on the starboard side of the fuselage.

The fin is of conventional construction, and on aircraft for the RAF it houses an integral fuel tank. The rudder is conventional.

The variable geometry wings swivel on cylindrical pivots coated in Teflon to reduce friction, and are driven by hydraulic actuators. Each wing has two pylons for external stores, and inboard heavy duty pylon and an outboard light duty pylon. These pylons are mounted on vertical pivots linked by tracking rods, and are arranged to swivel together to ensure they and the stores they carry remain end-on to the airflow regardless of the angle of sweep of the wings.

The wings are milled from solid billets of aluminium alloy, and have high-lift slats along the leading edge and double-slotted flaps along the trailing edge. When the high-lift devices are retracted the wings look ordinary enough, but the fact that there are no bumps or excrescences when everything is retracted is testimony to the skill of the Italian designers and engineers who built this part of the aircraft: airliners with similar double-slotted flaps have large fairings under the wing trailing edge to accommodate the extension mechanism. On a variable geometry wing such fairings are out of the question (like the underwing pylons, they would have to swivel to remain end-on to the airflow when the wing sweep angle is altered) and this greatly complicates the internal design. There is an integral fuel tank in each wing.

Each tailplane is mounted on a horizontal pivot and moves as an entire surface to provide control in flight. The surfaces operate as 'tailerons', moving up or down together to provide control in the elevator sense, or differentially to provide control in the aileron sense. Under maximum load the taileron hydraulic jacks will develop a total of 110hp — or as much as the Oberursal engine fitted to Manfred von Richthofen's Fokker Triplane in 1918!

When the wings are swept forward or nearly forward the tailerons alone do not provide a sufficiently crisp roll, so a spoiler on the upper surface of the down-going wing extends automatically to reduce lift on that side and speed the process.

If the electronic flying control system fails there is a mechanical mode which provides control of the aircraft using only the tailerons. As one pilot commented, 'In that condition the Tornado flies like a cow, it is not a very pleasant aeroplane, but at least it will get you home . . .'

The use of tailerons and spoilers to control the aircraft in roll leaves the full length of the wing trailing edge free for high-lift flaps, which work in conjunction with slats running the length of the leading edge. When the high-lift devices are fully deployed the lift coefficient of the Tornado's wing increases to a factor of 2.9, a commendably high figure. For comparison, the Buccaneer attack aircraft, a 1950s design with an innovative high-lift system using high pressure air from the engine compressors ducted over the flaps, achieved a lift coefficient of only 1.9. Thus the Tornado's system without flap blowing is about a third more efficient than that of the Buccaneer with this feature, which shows how much the design of high-lift systems advanced between the early 1950s and the late 1960s.

Tornados in the initial production batches were fitted with Turbo-Union RB199-34R Mk 101 three-spool turbofan engines which developed 9,000lb thrust in 'cold' power boosted to 16,000lb with reheat. Later aircraft are fitted with Mk 103 engines which deliver 5% more thrust.

Each engine is fitted with a thrust-reverser, which forms part of the integrated system designed to bring the aircraft to a halt safely but rapidly after landing. Dave Eagles explains how the system operates:

'For the shortest possible landing roll the pilot will "pre-arm" the thrust reversing system while on the landing approach, by rocking the throttles to the outboard position. Touch-down is at about 130kt, and once the aircraft's weight is on the main wheels this operates a micro-switch which makes a circuit to close the thrust reverser buckets at whatever power setting the engines happen to have at the time. Simultaneously the spoilers pop out above each wing to destroy the remaining lift and "glue" the aircraft on the runway. There is no bounce, and the aircraft will begin to decelerate immediately. If you then slam to maximum dry power you will get quite an impressive deceleration — not as good as an arrested deck landing, but the best one can do without wires!'

Should one pair of thrust reverser buckets fail to close while the other operates properly, the differential combination of forward and reverse thrusts would yaw the aircraft violently out of control in the direction of the working reverser. To prevent this the aircraft has a safety system which, if it detects such a failure, will immediately open the closed reverser buckets. If the pilot then applies maximum dry power the aircraft will get airborne again.

Those who fly the Tornado are enthusiastic about the roominess and quietness of its cockpits. There is plenty of room around each man and space for well-laid-out instrument panels. In fact the width of the fuselage was determined by the large nose diameter necessary to accommodate separate scanners for the attack and terrain-following radars — you might know it was not made that wide primarily for the benefit of the crew! In flight the cabin noise level is so low that the crew can converse in normal tones even when flying at 800kt IAS.

The Tornado IDS is a high performance swing-wing aircraft optimised for operations at low altitude and able to carry a reasonable bomb load. If that was all there was to it, the aircraft would not amount to much in military terms. High performance is of little value if the crew cannot find the target area or, having got there, they cannot hit the target with their weapons. Being able to fly at high speed at low altitude is of little value if the crew are tossed about to such an extent that they cannot function effectively, or if the aircraft is likely to fly into the ground. And even if the aircraft could perform all of these functions without restriction, it would not be of much value if enemy fighters and surface-to-air gun and missile systems could easily shoot it out of the sky.

When people talk about the complication and expense of the Tornado they are usually referring to the avionic systems it carries, each with a hi-tech sounding series of initials or acronym to denote its function. Complex and expensive they certainly are. Medieval alchemists dreamed of being able to transmute base metals into gold; in a sense the modern micro-electronic engineer has done it, fashioning base metals into systems which, weight for weight, are even more costly than gold. Small wonder the avionic systems — hidden out of sight in the bowels of the aircraft, complicated, hideously expensive and often misunderstood — are considered fair targets by those who wish to slash the cost of the aircraft.

Certainly the Tornado would have been a lot less expensive if many or most of its avionic systems had been omitted, but cost is only one side of the cost-effectiveness equation, and it is no exaggeration to say that these systems transform the Tornado from a mediocre attack aircraft into a devastatingly effective one. The impact of the microchip on military aviation has been even greater than on other aspects of modern life, giving a huge increase in the effectiveness of combat aircraft. A revolution has taken place, though it has left few outward signs of its passing. Apart from its swing-wing the Tornado does not *look* markedly different from aircraft built in the 1950s to perform similar roles. Nor are its brochure speed, climb, altitude or turning performance any great improvement on the best combat aircraft of the 1950s. But one cannot gauge the operational effectiveness of a combat aircraft from its external appearance nor from its brochure performance figures. In the remainder of this chapter we shall examine some areas where the Tornado's avionics systems give it a greatly improved operational capability compared with previous types of attack aircraft.

Right:
When all else fails . . . the arrester hook fitted to the Tornado, for emergency use if the aircraft has to be brought to a halt rapidly.

Above:
The ease of access included the radar installation, which opens up like the pages of a book.

Left:
The Tornado IDS carries two separate radar installations, with an attack radar (larger scanner) and a terrain-following radar (smaller scanner).

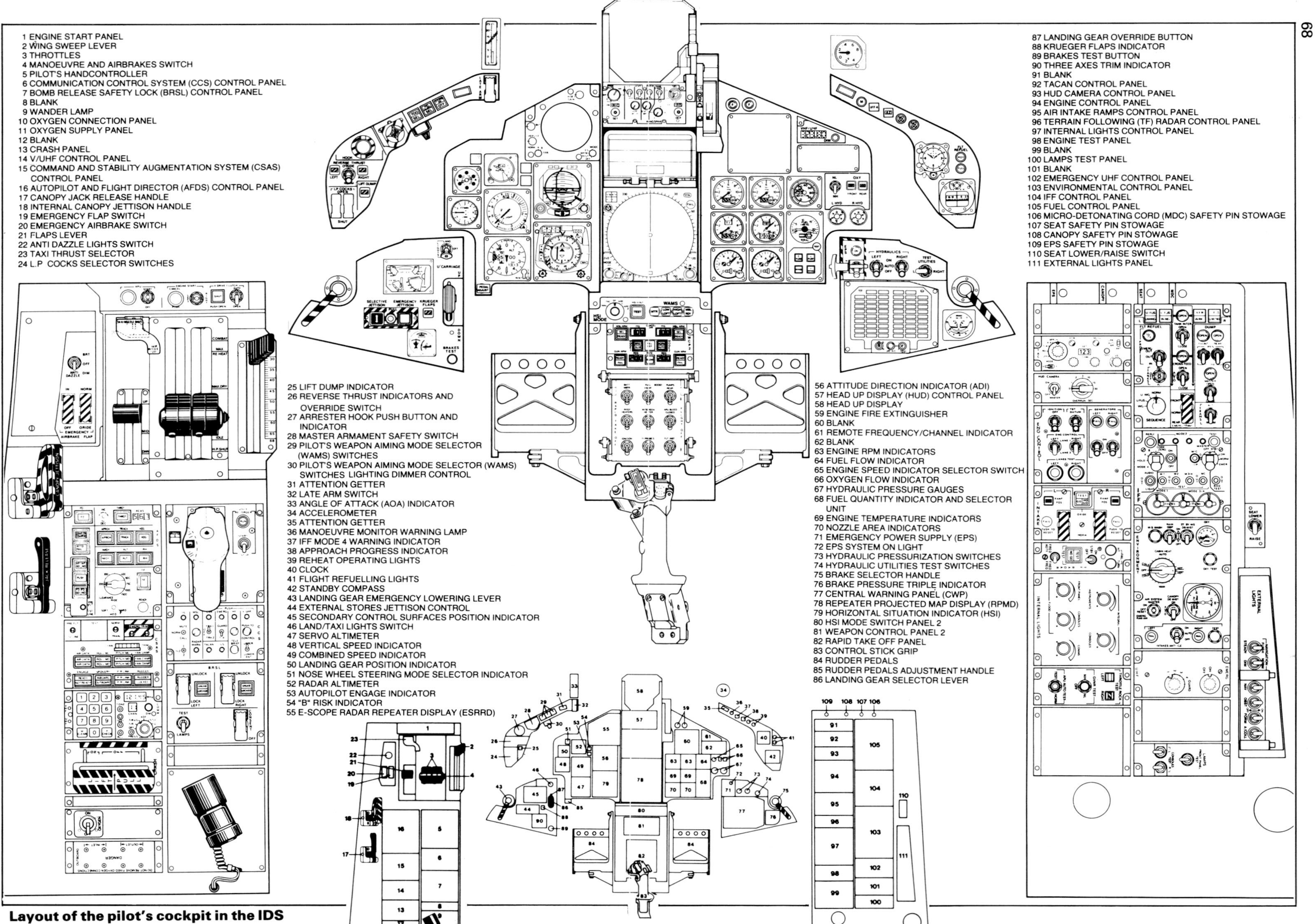

Layout of the pilot's cockpit in the IDS Tornado

Layout of the navigator's cockpit in the IDS Tornado.

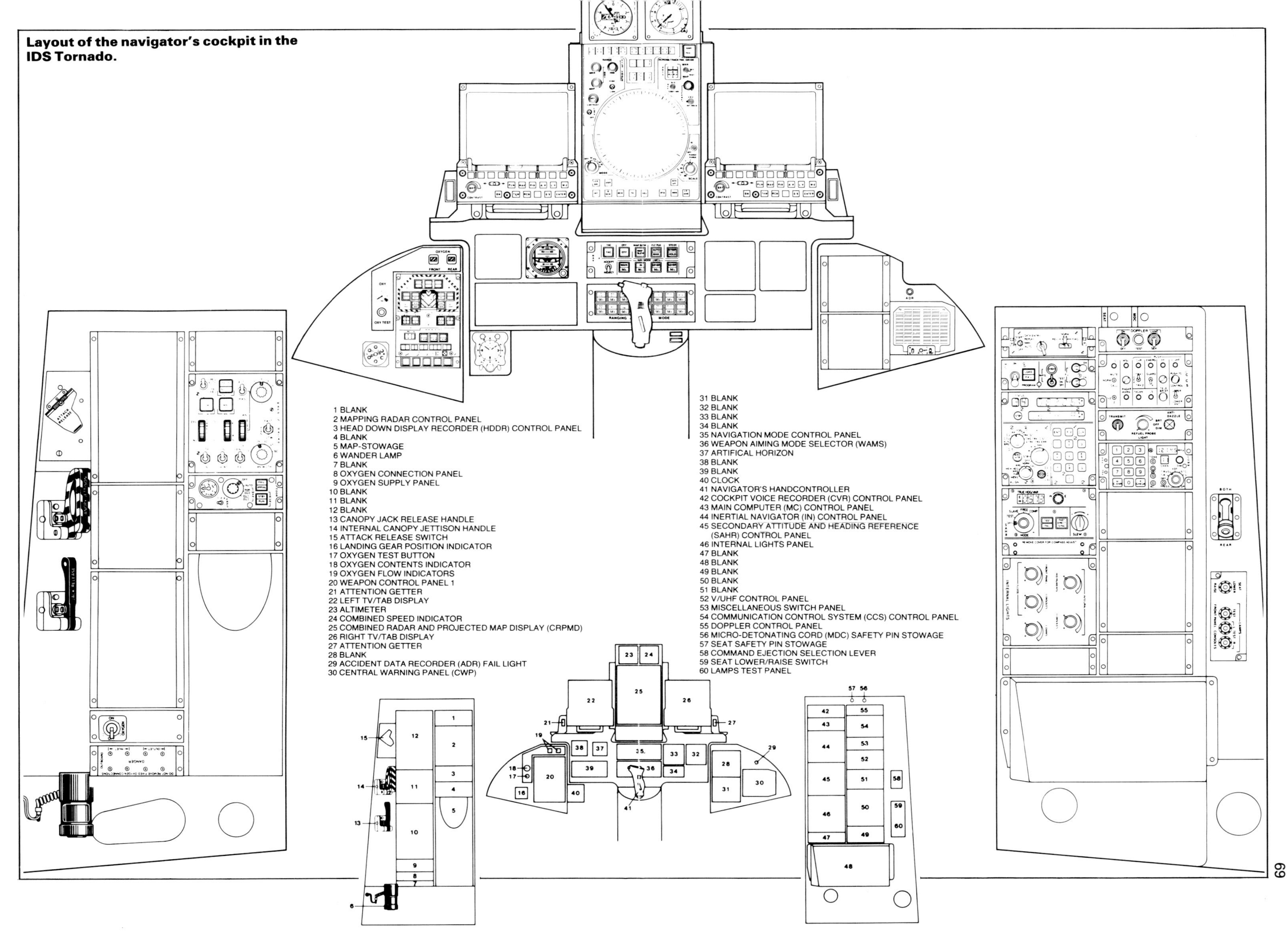

The Navigation and Attack System

The Tornado carries a sophisticated attack radar, an inertial navigation system, a Doppler navigation radar and a heading reference system, all of which feed the main navigation computer. By continually collating the velocity and positional information from the different sources, the computer maintains a running check on the aircraft's current and future positions. The computer uses this information to drive the moving map displays in front of the pilot and the navigator, on which they can see their true position and heading at any time during the flight. The navigator can switch on to his screen the picture from the attack radar, the moving map picture, or, if he wishes, he can show both together. On a smaller TV-type screen above the main screen the navigator can display his planned flight track and show details of the aircraft's actual track, its ground speed, the time-to-go to the next turning point or the target, and other flight parameters.

To get the most out of them, however, the modern electronic systems still require skilful handling. Inertial and Doppler navigational systems suffer from 'drift', which means that with time they become progressively less accurate. Moreover, they drift at different rates and in different ways, so that at times they will provide conflicting information on the position of the aircraft. Flt Lt Dick Middleton, a navigator with No 617 Squadron, explains:

'The navigation computer is programmed to give a different weight to each type of fix. The most accurate is what we call a "stand" fix, taken when the aircraft is standing on the ground over a point whose position has been accurately surveyed. At our airfield each aircraft shelter has its latitude and longitude, measured to a hundredth of a degree (about 60yd), painted on the wall; we have other surveyed points with this information at several locations around the airfield. Before we take off we feed two "stand" fixes into the computer, usually one in the shelter and one at the holding point just before entering the runway. That gives the computer an accurate datum from which to work.

'Once we are airborne the best fix is a radar fix. I can switch both the radar picture and the moving map picture on to the screen in front of me. The moving map indicates where the navigation computer thinks the aircraft is; the radar picture shows the real world in front of the aircraft, so that has to be the more accurate. By adjusting the moving map picture until it appears superimposed on the radar picture, I can update the navigation computer and take out any errors in the system.

'If for any reason we cannot use the attack radar for a fix the pilot can take one visually, using his hand controller to move a cross over a known point on the ground on his head-up display. For example, if we were flying near the coast he could use the end of a pier; or if we were inland he might use one end of a distinctive bridge over a river.'

If the navigator can see the target on radar he will place his bombing marker over it, and the computer will fly the aircraft accurately to the release position and drop the bombs automatically. Nevertheless, there are many types of target which do not show up distinctively on radar: for example those which are buried underground, or those situated amongst other objects which also produce radar echoes. To attack these the navigator carries out what is known as an offset attack: he selects an offset point near the target which will give a distinctive radar return, and feeds into the computer an accurate distance and bearing from that point to the target. When he reaches the target area he places his bombing marker over the offset point on his radar screen, and the computer will fly the aircraft to attack the real target as before.

Wg Cdr Grant McLeod, commanding No 17 Squadron, has first-hand operational flying experience of four generations of attack aircraft in the Royal Air Force: the Hunter, the Phantom, the Jaguar and the Tornado. He summed up the progressive improvement in operational capability brought by the new avionic systems:

'The Hunter was a very simple aircraft and navigation was by map and stopwatch. Even in good weather it was hard work for the pilot to get himself to the target area, find the pull-up point, get his sight on the target and attack with guns or rockets or bombs, then navigate home. Whether a pilot was successful in doing this depended to a great extent on his level of skil! and experience.

'The Phantom was a lot better. It carried a navigator, and there was a first-generation analogue computer and an early inertial navigation system to help us get to our targets and we could do so considerably more accurately and in rather worse weather than was possible in the Hunter.

'The Jaguar was only a single seater, but it was a better attack aircraft than the Phantom. It had a much more accurate inertial navigation system and a digital computer which could hold a lot more data and digest new data much more quickly. What that meant, in simple terms, was that in a Jaguar the average pilot was able to find his target in worse weather, and drop his bombs with greater accuracy, than he could have in a Hunter or a Phantom.

'The Tornado navigation system is a similar order of advance over that in the Jaguar. In terms of capability and accuracy, comparing the Tornado navigation system with that I flew with in the Phantom is like comparing an old fashioned pocket watch with a modern multi-function digital. It enables the Tornado to hit targets accurately in the worst of weather or at night.

'What difference does it make to the crew to have the more modern system? It is a question of workload. The Tornado crew can hand over much of the routine navigation of the aircraft to

Below:
ZA326, the sixth British trainer version, was severely damaged during ground running at Warton. The aircraft was issued to the RAE at Bedford in 1983.

the computer. They can let the computer navigate them to the target, confident that they are flying clear of known defended areas, on track and on time. That is a tremendous advantage. It gives the crew more time to manage their weapons system, the navigator can spend more time looking at his radar to up-date his computer, managing his electronic countermeasures equipment, keeping watch for enemy fighters, etc. It has taken a lot of the cockpit workload out of basic navigation. The bottom line of this is that we now see relatively inexperienced crews flying Tornado and producing quite outstanding bombing results.

'Yes, the Tornado is a very expensive aeroplane. But against a given target one needs fewer Tornados to achieve a given amount of damage, than if older types such as Phantoms or Jaguars were used: the Tornado weapon-aiming system is so much more accurate that a far lower proportion of the bombs will miss the target and be wasted.'

The Tornado's ability to attack targets with great accuracy has given a new lease of life to the old fashioned general purpose bomb. An often-quoted adage on bombing accuracy states that if the average bomb-aiming error throughout a raiding force can be halved, the effect of a given weight of attack will be quadrupled; so money spent on reducing bombing errors is usually money well spent. If a 1,000lb bomb is properly fused and correctly configured (ie with or without retardation, depending on the target), it has sufficient destructive power to wreck most types of target if it scores a direct hit or a very near miss. If a stick of 1,000pdrs can knock out a target, it is unnecessary to use guided missiles or other types of specialised weaponry which are many times more expensive.

Command & Stability Augmentation System

The primary flying control system fitted to the Tornado is a so-called Command & Stability Augmentation System (CSAS). The pilot's stick movements are converted into electronic control signals, which are passed via a computer to the actuators driving the control surfaces. If the aircraft is flying straight and level and (say) the pilot pulls back on the stick, he produces a demand for a rate of change of pitch. The computer compares the pilot's demand with the aircraft's actual pitch rate — initially zero — and directs both tailerons to begin moving down towards their full travel to bring up the nose at the required rate. The amount of taileron movement necessary to give that rate of pitch change will depend on the aircraft's speed and how heavily it is loaded. As soon as the nose of the aircraft is rising at the required rate, the computer detects this and moves the tailerons to hold that rate of change.

So far as the pilot is concerned, the system gives an aircraft with a very crisp but otherwise normal control response. Dave Eagles explains why the system is so useful:

'When you first fly the Tornado it feels like any other aeroplane. But the big advantage of the system is that it gives the same control characteristics under all conditions of flight, whether you are flying at 800kt or at 250kt, at 50,000ft or at 200ft, with bombs and tanks on or with them off. The Jaguar does not have that system; if you shove on stick to put it into a roll when the aircraft is clean it just whips round. But if you put on roll in a Jaguar whose wings are covered in bombs and tanks, it feels as if you are flying a Boeing 707!'

This system is particularly valuable when the Tornado IDS version is carrying the larger loads, such as JP233 or MW-1 weapons containers plus pairs of drop tanks, ECM pods and Sidewinder missiles. In this condition the aircraft is subjected to maximum speed and g limitations, but otherwise it handles almost exactly the same as when it is 'clean'.

Not only does the CSAS provide consistent manoeuvring rates throughout the Tornado's performance envelope, it is equally valuable when the pilot does not want to manoeuvre the aircraft at all — when he holds the stick in the central position for straight and level flight. If the aircraft runs into turbulence while flying at high speed at low altitude, for example, the violent up currents and down currents will try to knock the aircraft off the intended line of flight. The computer detects these changes the instant they start to occur and immediately moves the tailerons in the opposite direction, working continuously to smooth out each bump before it can develop. The computer makes these corrections far faster than a human being possibly could; in fact the Tornado's pilot, holding the stick in the central position and concentrating on other aspects of the mission, will often be unaware of the frenetic activity being conducted on his behalf by the tailerons, out of sight at the rear of the aircraft. The system is very popular with Tornado crews who, understandably, are keen to avoid the prolonged acute discomfort they would otherwise suffer.

The system also gives a marked improvement in effectiveness during operations in the low altitude attack role, as Capitano Sergio Burini of 6° Stormo has commented:

'Flying at high speed at low altitude in the Tornado is much more comfortable and far less fatiguing than in the F-104. Flying that type of mission over northern Italy in an F-104 on a hot bumpy day is like driving a car over an open field at 100km/hr, you have to slow down until the shaking you get falls to a level you can stand. A major factor limiting the time one can fly at high speed at low level in the F-104 is how long a pilot can stand being bounced about before his concentration starts to fail and things begin to get dangerous.

'In the Tornado the cockpit is much quieter and the flight control system compensates automatically for turbulence. In the Tornado you never have to slow down for turbulence; if it starts to get too bad you just put wings fully back and that makes the ride smoother. Having a comfortable ride is very important if you are flying a mission with two hours or more at very low altitude.'

Another area of the flight envelope where the CSAS plays an important part is at low speed. Here again, if the pilot holds his stick in the central position the automatic control system will do its utmost to hold the aircraft straight and level as instructed. Dave Eagles talked about the unnatural feeling this gives initially to Tornado pilots who have been used to conventional control systems:

'If you lower the flaps and slow down to about 115kt (indicated), at the onset of the stall one wing will drop. But it is very mild; the movement is opposed by the CSAS. You can look out over the wing, holding the stick in the central position, and see the spoilers flapping in and out trying to keep the wings level. The CSAS says to itself "the pilot does not want any attitude change", and if any rate of change appears it immediately moves the control surfaces in the opposite direction to counter it. The taileron and the spoilers flap up and down to keep the aeroplane steady, but the pilot feels nothing at all because the aircraft is flying straight and level. It is quite amazing.'

At the time of writing, test pilots at Warton are conducting trials with Spin Prevention Incidence Limiting System (SPILS), prior to its fitting in all Tornados. By setting maximum incidence levels for any given airspeed, SPILS sets limits for the flying control computer beyond which it will not take the aircraft. Thus if, in the heat of combat, the pilot attempts too violent a manoeuvre, SPILS will take the aircraft to its safe manoeuvre boundaries but will not allow it past them. In air-to-air combat aircraft often have to fly close to their manoeuvre limits, and if they exceed them the aircraft might 'depart' out of control leaving the crew no alternative but to eject. Hence the term 'carefree manoeuvring' is sometimes used to describe SPILS.

Automatic Terrain-Following System

Quite separate from the attack radar, the Tornado is fitted with a terrain-following radar. This is integrated with the navigational computer and automatic pilot, and is able to fly the aircraft along a pre-planned route at high speed at 200ft without the pilot having to touch the controls. Thus, the aircraft can hug the ground, shielded by darkness or poor visibility, safe from many forms of attack. When flying on automatic terrain-following the pilot can select one of three types of ride: soft, medium and hard. The soft ride is selected when the aircraft is over friendly territory or passing through relatively lightly defended areas; the aircraft follows the general line of the contours and smooths over hills and obstacles in its path without trying to follow their contours too abruptly. The hard ride setting is used when the aircraft is passing through heavily defended areas, when it is essential to follow ground undulations as closely as possible to exploit their cover; but even in the Tornado there is a limit to how long a crew can work effectively when being bounced about in this way. The medium ride setting is for use when conditions are between the two extremes.

In service the Tornado's automatic terrain-following system has proved extremely reliable. Nevertheless, crews need a period of 'education' before they are asked to entrust their lives to it, as Oberstleutnant Walther Jertz of Jagdbombergeschwader 31 explains:

'You have to learn to trust the system, you don't just get into the aircraft and fly on terrain-following radar at 200ft at night. You start off by flying the aircraft on automatic terrain-following at 1,000ft by day to give you confidence that the system really works. During our initial daylight flights we point the aircraft at high towers and hills to see if the terrain-following radar reacts, and, of course, it does. Then we take the aircraft down in steps to 500ft, that is as low as we are allowed to fly with it over Germany in peacetime. When you have flown with it at low altitude often enough you come to trust the system. Then you do the same thing at night. Finally, crews go to Goose Bay [in Canada] where they can fly over uninhabited areas at 200ft at night or in poor weather.'

Penetrating the Defences

By penetrating enemy defences at high speed and keeping low to get maximum cover from folds in the ground, the Tornado is able to keep out of reach of the longer-range surface-to-air missile systems and make fighter interception extremely difficult. The ability to navigate accurately further reduces the aircraft's vulnerability, enabling the crew to route themselves clear of known enemy defensive concentrations. Doing those things at night or in poor visibility means that an enemy has to use radar to engage the aircraft, in which case the Tornado's radar warning receiver should detect its signals in time for the crew to take effective evasive action. During attack missions, Tornado IDS crews would normally go to pains to avoid enemy fighters, but if cornered they would fight back using cannon and Sidewinder missiles.

If the Tornado is attacking a target of importance it will usually have to fight its way past short range surface-to-air missile and gun defences to reach its objective. However, time is short for the defenders, and if the low-level attackers employ electronic countermeasures the difficulties of engaging them are compounded.

The Tornado's main electronic countermeasures devices are carried on the outer-wing stations: a Sky Shadow jamming pod under the port wing of RAF aircraft (German and Italian Air Force aircraft carry the essentially similar Cerberus pod) and a BOZ dispenser pod under the starboard wing.

The Sky Shadow pod is about 11ft long and 14in in diameter and carries built-in receivers. Incoming radar signals are fed into a microprocessor which compares them against a library of radar signal characteristics. Within less than half a second the microprocessor will identify the type or types of radar and place them in order of danger to the aircraft (for example, a gun control radar trying to lock on to the aircraft would receive a higher priority than a missile control radar in the search mode). The transmitters will then radiate jamming or deceptive signals to counter the greatest threats. The pod contains two separate transmitters, with aerials at the front and the rear to beam jamming in those directions (usually an attack starting from the side will quickly end up in the aircraft's rear quadrant). Both transmitters will usually feed one aerial to radiate maximum power in that direction; but if there are threat radars in both the forward and rear hemispheres, both aerials will radiate the appropriate jamming or spoofing signals. The microprocessor will continually review the electronic situation around the aircraft, automatically retuning the transmitters to the most threatening radars and switching them between the aerials to provide the greatest possible protection for the aircraft. Immediately threat radar signals are no longer being received, the pod will cease jamming.

Similar in length to Sky Shadow but small in diameter, the BOZ pod houses a dispenser for expendables — chaff and infra-red decoy flares. Modern chaff is quite different from the old-fashioned 'Window', and the strips — each finer than a human hair — are made of fibreglass coated with a thin layer of aluminium. The BOZ can push out chaff very rapidly, to distort the aim of radar-aimed guns or missiles, and is at its most effective if used in conjunction with jamming and an evasive manoeuvre. If an infra-red homing missile is launched at the Tornado from the ground or by an enemy fighter, at the press of a button the BOZ will eject a string of decoy flares to seduce the missiles away.

If the underwing pods can delay the lock-on of an enemy fire-control radar by 10sec, in that time a Tornado flying at 600kt will cover just over 1½ miles. In the time it takes for a radar to complete its lock-on, produce accurate fire control data, and for the missile to travel four miles, the aircraft could cover a further 1½ miles again. Often those three miles covered will be sufficient to take a low-flying Tornado behind the safety of the next undulation in the ground, behind trees or buildings, or out of range of the enemy weapon system. And even if the enemy radar does achieve a lock-on, deceptive signals from the jamming pod, or chaff, could induce errors into the enemy fire control process sufficient to let the aircraft through unscathed. The inaccuracy need not be large: an angular error of only ¼° in aligning a radar on the aircraft at a range of four miles could cause the shells or missiles to miss by 100ft, putting the aircraft outside their sphere of lethality when they detonated.

TORNADO FLYING CONTROLS

Above left:
The taileron shown in the maximum nose-up position.

Above:
The taileron incidence scale, painted in pink.

Left and below:
The wing in the take-off configuration, with leading edge slats lowered and trailing edge flaps in the mid-position.

Above and right:
The wing in the landing configuration with the Kruger leading edge flaps (inboard of the swing wing) and leading edge slats lowered, and trailing edge flaps fully down. The wing spoilers are seen raised, as they would be after touch-down to destroy lift from the upper surface of the wing.

Below:
The port airbrake extended.

TORNADO VARIABLE GEOMETRY

Above:
The wings are shown in the 25° (slow speed flight), the 45° (normal manoeuvring) and the 67° (high speed dash) sweep configurations.

Right:
A view from above the wing root, showing the flexible finger plates which fair over the moving joint between the wing and the fuselage.

Below:
The seal used to fair the wing trailing edge where it moves into the fuselage.

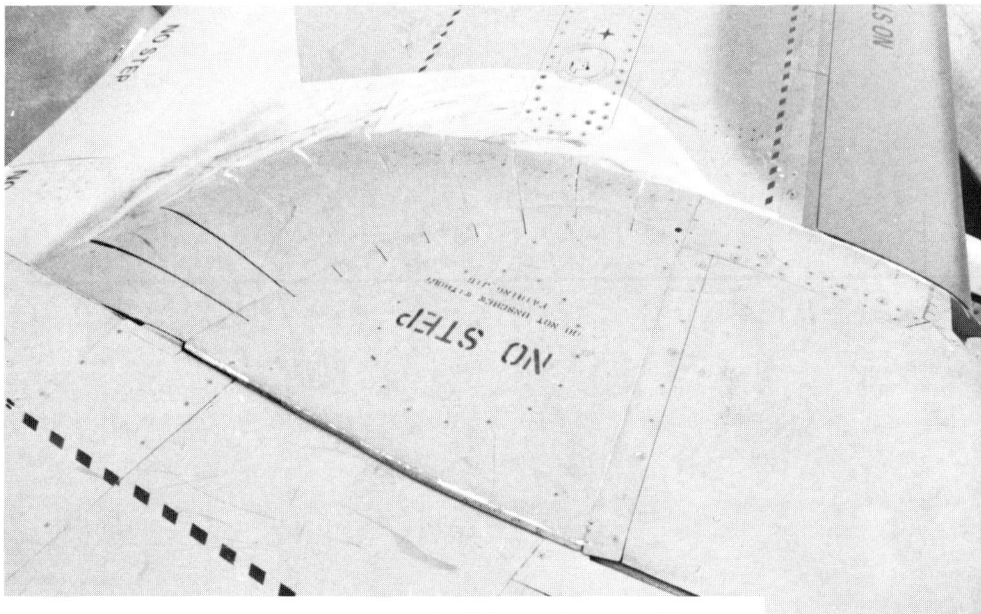

TORNADO CLOSE-UPS

Left and below left:
Detail of the port wing tank pylon and Sidewinder missile rail. The tank's fins are to force the tank cleanly away from the aircraft on release.

Right:
The Laser Ranger & Marked Target Seeker, fitted to the starboard of the nose wheel door on IDS Tornados for the RAF. Above the LRMTS is the muzzle of the starboard 27mm Mauser cannon.

Bottom left:
The in-flight refuelling probe retracted into its fairing along the starboard side of the canopy. When not required, the entire assembly can be removed.

Below:
Although Tornados flying operational missions would return with drop tanks if possible, they would jettison them if they were engaged by enemy fighters. Each HAS (Hardened Aircraft Shelter) holds a small stock of replacement tanks.

EMERGENCY CANOPY REMOVAL

Below:
In an emergency the canopy can be jettisoned by two rockets, which lift the forward end so the airflow pulls it clear. Additionally, to enable the crew to escape if the plane is on the ground and there is insufficient airflow to lift the canopy clear, a miniature detonating cord (MDC) is embedded along the length of the canopy. The MDC fires automatically when an ejector seat handle is pulled, or it can be activated separately from the cockpit. In addition there is an emergency external system to fragment the canopy to enable the crew to be rescued, operated from the port side of the cockpit.

BOMBING UP THE TORNADO

The procedures and the equipment for loading bombs on the Tornado were designed so the operation could take place inside the confined space of a HAS. Here Cpl Al Banks leads a team of armourers to demonstrate loading of a 1,000lb bomb on a Tornado of No 617 Squadron. For the photographer the operation was performed in the open, though normally this would not be the case.

Left:
The bomb is pushed to the aircraft on a bomb stillage, a purpose-built wheeled frame designed to support the weapon and enable it to be manoeuvred easily.

Below left and bottom left:
When bombs are released from high-speed aircraft, the airflow may prevent them falling away cleanly under gravity, causing them to miss the target by a wide margin. Because of this, modern attack aircraft employ cartridge ejection systems to thrust the bomb cleanly away from the aircraft. As a safety measure the ejection cartridge is removed before the bomb is lifted to the rack.

Below:
On RAF Tornados the MACE (minimum area crutchless ejector) system is employed for the carriage of bombs. Before the bomb was brought to the HAS, two block-shaped MACE saddles were fitted on it; these remain on the bomb when it is released.

Top right:
Next, a Type Y loader is pushed into position under the bomb. A hand-operated hydraulic lift is then used to raise the bomb, still on its stillage, into position just beneath the bomb rack.

Bottom right:
The bomb is raised up to the rack, and internal clamps lock around the MACE saddles.

MAR II

MAR II

Right:
A safety pin, with warning flag, is inserted in the rack to prevent accidental release of the bomb on the ground, and the ejection cartridge is inserted.

Below right:
One of the armourers sets the plane's load on the Weapon Programming Unit situated under the port air intake.

Bottom:
The operation is complete. Note the aerodynamically clean installation permitted by MACE. There are no drag-producing crutches, necessary on previous systems to prevent the bomb rocking from side to side on its carrier.

TORNADO REFUELLING

Left and below:
Connecting the refuelling nozzle to the aircraft. The wire running along the ground is used to earth the plane and the refuelling vehicle, a necessary precaution to prevent sparking and possible fire due to a build-up of static electricity.

Bottom:
The hose in place, SAC John Turner demonstrates the simplicity of refuelling the Tornado. All tanks are filled via the single NATO connector, through which fuel flows under pressure at a rate of 2,400lb/min. Controlled from the panel above the connector, the tanks are filled in order from the front and to rear. The fin tank is always filled last: if it were filled first, the aircraft might become tail-heavy and sit on its rear end.

TORNADO PILOT'S PRE-FLIGHT CHECK

Above:

Shown are items, a few of many, checked by Flt Lt Bill Harrison of No 617 Squadron during his systematic pre-flight check of the Tornado. A visual check confirms the plane had been fitted with the external stores (tanks, bombs, ECM pods) necessary for the mission it is to fly. A glance over the area of concrete beneath the plane confirms the absence of wet patches betraying fuel, oil or hydraulic leaks. The warning flags are attached to pins which must be removed before take-off.

Centre right:

A close-up of the jet pipe and afterburner nozzle.

Right:

Inspection of the gun bay. During flights on which the cannon are not to be fired, the pilot checks that the electrical firing plug to each is disconnected.

Far right, top:

Checking the port main tyre for excessive wear.

Far right, bottom:

A hop to check the inside of each air intake is clear of foreign objects. It would not be the first time a thoughtless individual had used an intake as a convenient shelf on which to leave spanners, etc. When the engines start such items are devoured immediately, and can wreck the delicate innards.

DANGER INTAKE
KEEP CLEAR

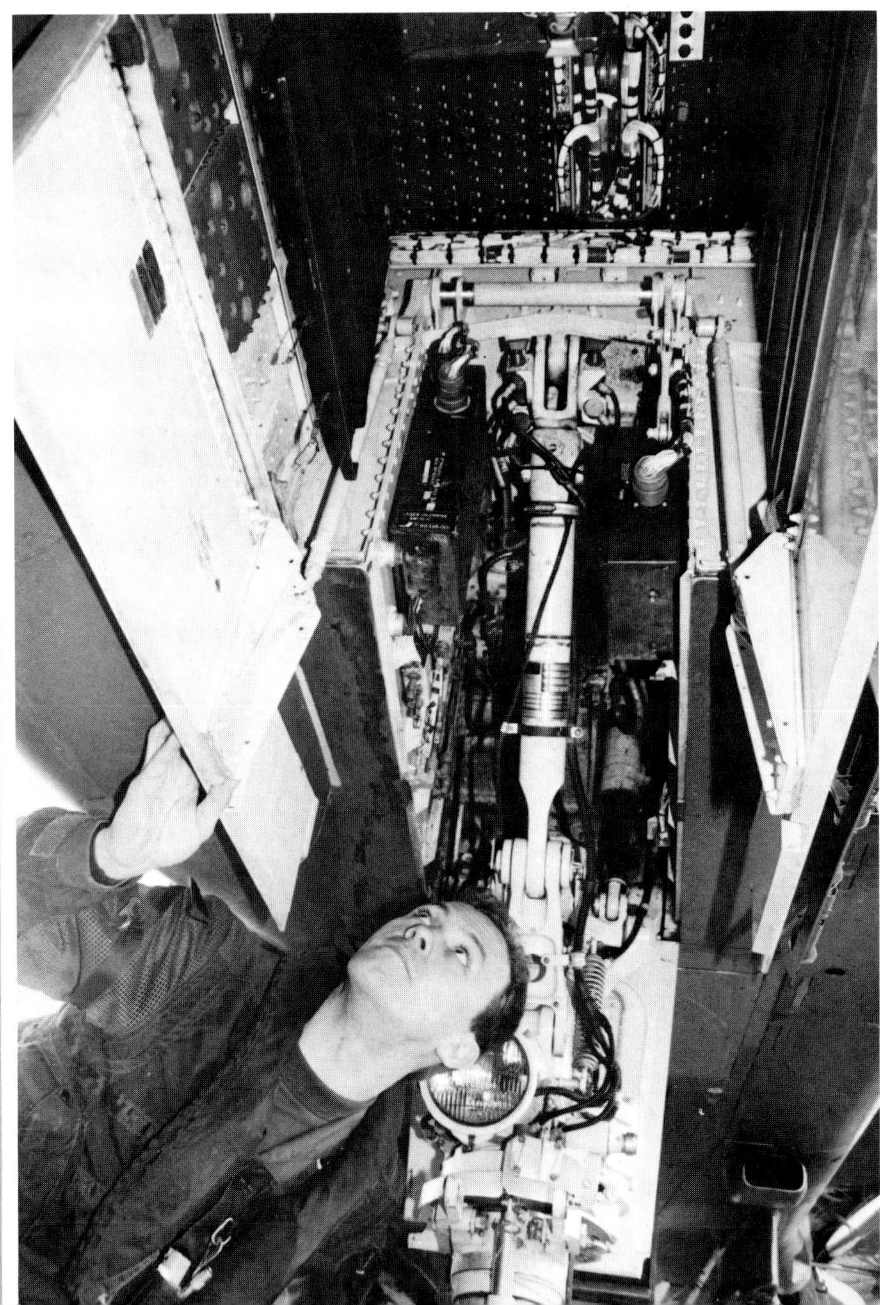

This page:
A check of the nose-wheel assembly and nose-wheel bay.

7 Tornado IDS Joins the Ranks

Shortly after they signed the Tornado production contract the three national defence ministries agreed that all crew conversion training should take place at the same school, the Tri-national Tornado Training Establishment (TTTE). The Royal Air Force airfield at Cottesmore in the Midlands of England was chosen for this purpose, and in April 1978 the first personnel arrived there to begin preparations to receive the new aircraft.

Early in 1980 the first two service crews, one each from the Royal Air Force and the German Air Force, arrived at Manching to learn to fly the Tornado before going to Cottesmore to form the kernel of the instructional staff there. On these people would depend the success or failure of the introduction of the new aircraft into service, and as might be expected they were picked men with considerable flying experience. Wg Cdr Bob O'Brien, the Chief Instructor designate, had some 2,900 flying hours in fast jets. Sqn Ldr Vaughan Morris, the Senior Navigator, had 2,000 hours on Buccaneers; Major Hartmut Jung, destined to command the Standards Squadron, had flown 2,000 hours in the F-104; Maj Bernd von Sivers had more than 1,700 hours experience navigating RF-4Es. By July the ground training was complete and the two crews began flying the Tornado under instruction from Panavia test pilots. Soon five more service pilots and two navigators followed them through the course at Manching.

Also in July 1980, Gp Capt Mick Simmons arrived at Cottesmore to take command, and shortly afterwards the unit's first two Tornados, a trainer and an attack aircraft, arrived from Warton. New aircraft were emerging from the assembly hangars at Warton and Manching at a rate of about eight per month, and by December there were 11 Tornados at Cottesmore.

In February 1981 the first official conversion course began at Cottesmore, to train further instructors, and by the following October the TTTE had a total of 28 pilots and 19 navigators certified as 'Competent to Instruct'.

Below:
A German and an Italian Tornado undergoing maintenance in the hangar at Cottesmore.

One of the original pilots to go through the course at Manching, who joined the core of instructors in Cottesmore in November 1980, was Oberstleutnant Klaus Kahlert of the German Air Force. He described the mood at the training establishment:

'In my view the important thing about the TTTE at Cottesmore is that for the first time in NATO we had three nations working together as equals to meet a common goal. No nation was superior to the other two. Before that only the Royal Air Force did all the training of its own people; the German and Italian pilots were trained in the USA. Starting from scratch the three nations developed a common training philosophy for Tornado, with a common training syllabus.

'All sorts of questions had to be resolved. For example, during tactical formation flying how far apart should the aircraft fly? There was a difference in philosophy between the RAF on the one hand, and the German and Italian Air Forces with an American background on the other. There were differences on what to do when certain types of enemy threat were encountered. When should the formation run away, and when should it stay and fight? Those are questions of philosophy. We had to decide the common line we would teach to all the new crews.

'In a national air force the decision is taken to do things in a certain way and that is the way they are done. With three nations acting as equals everything had to be discussed not three times but maybe six or 10 times. But at the end of it we would have a compromise solution which contained the best aspects of each nation's arguments. It started as an experiment but it quickly went far beyond that stage, and it worked tremendously well.

'Once the training courses started we had people from the three nations come to Cottesmore from different backgrounds and with different experience levels. At the TTTE everything is tri-national. Everybody flies with everybody. It is quite common to have, say, an Italian pilot flying with a German navigator in a Tornado with British markings. The pilots and navigators are trained separately to the point where they can operate the aircraft safely, then they come together and fly as a student crew.'

Below:
Groundcrewmen at the TTTE changing the engine of a Tornado, showing the degree of accessibility and the minimal amount of specialised equipment necessary.

This page:
Scenes at the German Tornado weapons training unit, the Waffenausbildungskomponente (WaKo), the first Luftwaffe unit to receive Tornados.

Serving in the Royal Air Force

The first solely RAF unit to operate the new aircraft was the Tornado Weapons Conversion Unit at Honington, which began to form in June 1981. As in the case of the TTTE before it, the first step was to train the complement of instructors. Following that, the first course for trainee crews began in January 1982. Crews learned to operate the aircraft in combat, practising low altitude flying, tactical formation flying and fighter evasion, and laydown and toss bombing attacks.

No 9 Squadron of the RAF was the first operational unit in any air arm to convert to the Tornado. It had a distinguished record dating back to December 1914 and had previously operated the Vulcan, the RAF type in most urgent need of replacement. Wg Cdr Peter Gooding assumed command of the squadron in May 1982 and later told the author:

'When the squadron started to form at Honington we had six or seven aeroplanes and only three crews to fly them, until the people on the next course at the Weapons Conversion Unit completed their training. When we received the aircraft they were fully equipped and virtually ready to go to war, they had a full complement of radar and other avionics. The guns needed some modifications before we could fire them, but had there been a war we could have used them.

'The crews came through the Weapons Conversion Unit at a steady rate, and the last arrived on the unit in October 1982. With one exception they were all very experienced, from a range of backgrounds. We had four Lightning pilots, a couple who had flown Jaguars, a few Buccaneer pilots and two had flown Phantoms. Most of the navigators came from Buccaneers, Phantoms or Vulcans. We also had one guy on his first tour, a navigator who had done outstandingly well during training.'

At the beginning of September 1982, while the squadron training programme was at an early stage, Peter Gooding was asked to send six Tornados to take a short part in the Farnborough Air Display. There had been no time for the service pilots to work up a proper display routine so the aircraft swept past the crowd at 5sec intervals with wings fully back, cut in reheat and accelerated away from the airfield; immediately they were clear of the airfield the Tornados had to cut out reheat, to avoid breaking the sound barrier over the town of Farnborough — and a lot more besides.

By now other RAF squadrons were also beginning to convert to the Tornado: in the summer of 1982 No 617 Squadron, the famous 'Dam Busters', and shortly afterwards No 27 Squadron, began assembling aircraft and crews at Marham.

With the demise of the four-engined Vulcan bomber it might have appeared that the RAF had lost the capability to attack distant targets. The Falklands conflict, during which the Vulcans' extended-range attacks had played an important part, was still fresh in everybody's mind and the RAF was keen to demonstrate to the Argentinians and everyone else who cared to listen that it could still fly such missions

Left:
Wg Cdr Peter Gooding, Commander of No 9 Squadron when it became the first operational unit to receive the Tornado.

Below:
A No 27 Squadron Tornado GR1 approaches Nellis after a 'Green Flag' mission. *Frank Mormillo*

Above:
ZA562 of No 27 Squadron en route to the bombing ranges during 'Green Flag'. *Frank Mormillo*

if the occasion demanded. Although No 9 Squadron was still working up and far from ready for operations, Peter Gooding was ordered to lay on a dummy attack on the airfield at Akrotiri in Cyprus, from Honington. The flight would involve a round trip of 4,300 nautical miles, taking fuel from Victor tankers and a Buccaneer along the route.

'At the time I was given the task we had not started training for air-to-air refuelling. So it was a matter of picking the crew with most recent experience in air-to-air refuelling, and they worked up for the mission. The Tornado had never flown such a long mission and we had to fly a rehearsal around Britain to show that it was possible. We knew fuel would not be a problem provided the aircraft could find the tankers, but we were concerned whether it carried sufficient oil and oxygen.'

The rehearsal revealed no major problems, and on 8 November Flt Lts Ian Dugmore and Mike Holmes flew the mission. They cruised over France and southern Italy and past Crete at high altitude, descended to 200ft for a high speed low level dash over the final 100 miles to the target, withdrew at low altitude and then climbed to altitude for

Above and right:
A GR1 of No 617 Squadron, the second operational RAF unit to receive the type, being prepared for a sortie at Marham. Under the nose this aircraft carries a laser ranger and marked target designator, which became standard on operational British IDS aircraft.

the return flight. The Tornado was airborne for 12hr 10min and the flight went off with no major hitches.

As in the case of any advanced new aircraft, the introduction of the Tornado into front-line service was accompanied by the usual bout of teething troubles as squadron personnel struggled to learn the foibles of the new aircraft. Peter Gooding recalls:

'That first winter we had severe problems with the shortage of spare parts, they were slow to come through. Everything was new and it was difficult to get the amount of flying we needed to work up the squadron. But we had very experienced groundcrews who learned quickly, and the time needed to repair defects fell amazingly. Gradually the spares problems eased and in March 1983 we achieved for the first time our target for flying hours. From then we never looked back.

'With Tornado we had a new aeroplane with a weapons system that was a tremendous jump ahead of anything that had gone before. The firm's test pilots and those at Boscombe Down had proved that the various aspects of the system worked. But it is only when you get operational crews handling the aircraft that you discover what the kit will really do. I was always on the look-out for aspects of the aeroplane that needed modifying, but there was nothing major. We were trying new things the whole time, seeking to discover which procedures would work and which wouldn't. Bit by bit our capability improved. We had regular discussions on which procedures gave the best results; we adopted these for the squadron and wrote them into the standard operating procedures for units to follow.

'The thing that was uppermost in my mind throughout that tour was the big advance in capability the Tornado had brought to the Royal Air Force. It could do the things that other aircraft like the Phantom and the Jaguar and the Buccaneer had been doing, but it could do them very accurately at night or in bad weather. That applied not only to the attack phase of the mission, but the penetration phase as well. Jaguars and Buccaneers fly in formation by day. We had to devise ways of flying in formation at night when we couldn't see each other. We had the kit to do it, we could keep very accurate time spacing and very accurate track spacing. We began flying formations similar to those which other aircraft flew when they could see each other, and we would do the same thing at night or in cloud when you couldn't see the other aircraft. In war this would give an important advantage: against a defended target like an airfield, if several aircraft attack simultaneously in a co-ordinated manner they can saturate the defences.'

During 1983 No 9 Squadron steadily expanded its activities. In February it sent the first of several detachments to Germany, and in April a detachment went to Norway. On 1 July No 9 Squadron was declared operational, and took its place in the NATO Order of Battle as a night and all-weather attack squadron. The squadron conducted its first TACEVAL (tactical evaluation) in September, in the course of which one of its pilots was killed in a tragic accident. On 29 September Sqn Ldr Mike Stephens, one of the flight commanders, was returning at high altitude over the North Sea from a night sortie when the

Above:
A No 617 Squadron GR1 taxys out from the Nellis AFB flightline for a 'Green Flag' mission in 1986. *Frank Mormillo*

Tornado's electrical system suffered a complete failure. The pilot reverted to manual control of the aircraft but the engines, being electrically controlled, both failed and this led to a run down of the hydraulic system. As the aircraft descended through 15,000ft it was clear there was no hope of getting it down safely and the pilot told the navigator to eject. The latter did so, but for some reason which was never discovered, the pilot never followed. The Tornado plunged into the ground near Sandringham in Norfolk. The death of Mike Stephens was a personal loss to the author, who had flown with him many times while both served on No 360 Squadron some 10 years earlier.

That was the third Tornado crash, and the first one to be caused by a failure of the aircraft. Following the accident, Tornados were not formally grounded, but there was no flying for about a week while ground engineers carried out a minute examination of the aircraft's electrical system. Afterwards there were detailed changes to the system and the servicing procedures were amended; there has been no recurrence of the failure.

Shortly after his Tornados resumed flying, Peter Gooding led an eight-aircraft detachment to Goose Bay in northeastern Canada for low flying training.

'We went to Goose Bay to consolidate our training and to practice using the terrain-following system at low altitude at night and in bad weather. And we wanted to practice our low level tactics to see that they worked. If we had tried to fly over the United Kingdom or Germany in a formation spread across several miles, there is hardly anywhere we could go without passing into places we had to avoid — airfields, hospitals, danger areas, etc. And at night or in bad weather there was the danger of running into other aircraft. Over northern Canada we could fly in formation for long periods at low altitude, including flight at 600kt [0.9 Mach] at 200ft.

'The autopilot controls the aircraft during the terrain-following phase of the flight and crews had to develop confidence in the autopilot. There has never been a dangerous failure in the Tornado's terrain-following or autopilot systems which threatened to crash the aircraft. If there is a malfunction you get a very abrupt pull-up, and you find yourself heading for the stars at a very high rate.'

With Tornado production now getting into its stride at Warton, the re-equipment of the main body of RAF attack squadrons in Germany could begin in earnest. No 15 Squadron at Laarbruch began receiving the type in July 1983, followed by No 16 Squadron in December and No 20 Squadron in May 1984. The second base to receive the new aircraft was Brüggen, and its resident squadrons, No 14, No 17 and No 31, began their conversions in 1985. A reconnaissance unit, No 2 Squadron based at Laarbruch, is due to convert to the Tornado during 1988.

As mentioned in the Prologue, No 617 Squadron entered a four-aircraft team in the USAF Strategic Air Command Bombing & Navigation Competition in October 1984, which gained first and second places in the Le May Trophy for the best overall score by an individual crew, second place in the Mathis Trophy for the best score by a two-aircraft team, and first and third places in the Meyer Trophy for the highest damage expectancy by a pair of F-111s or Tornados. In the following year No 27 Squadron entered a team which did even better, taking first and second places in the Le May Trophy, second place in the Mathis Trophy and first and second places in the Meyer Trophy.

The results achieved by Tornado in the Strategic Air Command bombing competitions demonstrated that it could navigate with great accuracy and exact timing through a series of bomb release positions, and do so at least as well as any other type of all-weather attack aircraft. Nonetheless, the necessarily precise rules of the competition introduced many factors which would not be present in time of war, and by themselves the results did not give a

true indication of the combat effectiveness of the aircraft involved. A far better measure of the Tornado's combat effectiveness came in March 1985 when No 9 Squadron sent a detachment to take part in 'Green Flag', an elaborate training exercise against simulated Soviet weapons systems run by the US Air Force at Nellis, Nevada. Peter Gooding considered this realistic training particularly valuable:

'I do not belittle the achievements of the Tornado crews in the bombing competition: they did outstandingly well. But a bombing competition is not an operational exercise, whereas "Green Flag" is the closest we in the RAF get to a real war scenario. To me that first "Green Flag" exercise was an important milestone for the Tornado. At the end of each day's exercise there was a great debrief on the missions we had flown. They had video film of us going in to attack our targets, and trying to evade the air and ground defensive systems. We were assessed on how well our aircraft did against the various threats, and how accurately we put our bombs on the targets while avoiding those threats. "Green Flag" gave us a lot of confidence in our equipment and our training, it showed we were doing things right.'

A detachment to Nellis to take part in the 'Green Flag' or the generally similar 'Red Flag' exercises now forms an essential part of the crew training programme of all RAF Tornado IDS squadrons.

Above:
During 1985 Royal Air Force Tornado squadrons began to receive the JP233 airfield denial weapon, designed specifically for use with this aircraft. The GR1 carries two of these containers under the fuselage, each of which holds 30 SG357 runway cratering bombs and 215 HB876 area denial mines to hinder repair work.

The first RAF crews to fly Tornados either had considerable previous flying experience or had come straight from training having passed out top of their courses. In the nature of things such exceptional people are in short supply in any air force, and the Tornado would not be successful in service if only a small proportion of the available air-crew could be trained to handle it effectively. In 1984 Wg Cdr Dick Bogg took command of No 31 Squadron at Brüggen as it re-formed with Tornados (it will be remembered that as a Flight Lieutenant attached to NAMMA 14 years earlier, he had watched the start of work on the centre section of the first MRCA at the MBB plant at Augsburg). He told the author of his feelings when he learned that some of the crews posted to his unit would have little previous flying experience:

'Before it entered service there were some in the RAF who believed the Tornado would be so complicated that only experienced or exceptional crews should be allowed to fly it at first. We sometimes say that when a new aircraft comes in, we won't let first-tourists near it for the first five years or so. Well, I have four crews, pilots and navigators, doing their first tours on my squadron and they cope with the Tornado very well. Like most squadron commanders I was a bit worried when I was told I would have to take some first-tourists when the squadron re-formed with Tornados. Any squadron commander would prefer to have experienced crews — who wouldn't — but there are not enough experienced people to go around and No 31 Squadron has had to take its share of first-tourists. And I have been delighted with their performance. Their technical and flying performance has been very good, which speaks well for the people coming through our aircrew training system.

'The Tornado is quite complicated, it takes a long time to understand fully what the automatic systems are doing and why. Some crews are still not fully on top of all aspects of the aeroplane but that is what training is all about; it takes a long time to work up a new squadron to combat-ready status.

'To date, Tornado systems performance has been very good and we are getting excellent results. However, despite the 10 years of experience we now have with the aircraft, we're still not getting the most out of the Tornado. It still has enormous potential and the RAF probably has five years' work ahead of it to wring the best out of the total weapons system.'

The offensive counter-air mission — attacks on enemy airfields and related targets — is one of the main war roles of the RAF Tornado IDS squadrons. Air Marshal Sir Patrick Hine, until recently commander of NATO's 2nd Allied Tactical Air Force (which includes all RAF units in Germany), explained to the author the importance of such operations if Warsaw Pact forces ever launched a major attack on western Europe:

'With the numerical imbalance between the NATO and the Warsaw Pact air forces in the Central Region, we could not expect to gain air superiority by remaining on the defensive. Following the initial attacks by the enemy, we would go on to the offensive ourselves by hitting his airfields hard. The aim would be to reduce the number of sorties the enemy could mount against our airfields and our ground forces. In that way we would hope to throw the enemy air forces off balance and wrest the initiative from them. So that would be our broad philosophy: first to absorb the initial intensive enemy attacks, then as soon as we could to go out and hit his airfields and pin down his aircraft.

'If we were able to close some of their most important airfields, for example those operating "Fencers" or "Floggers", let us say for only 12 hours, then during that time none of the aircraft at those bases would be able to fly against us even though they were fully serviceable, sitting in their concrete shelters. Several hundred aircraft could be bottled up in that way.'

Wg Cdr Grant McLeod, the commander of No 17 Squadron, explains in greater detail how such attacks might be carried out:

'Look at a plan of a typical modern hardened military airfield and you will see it has certain characteristics. The runway is longer and much wider than necessary for take-offs and landings, so that even if part of it is cratered a usable strip might remain. Parallel to the runway is a taxiway long enough for aircraft to take-off and land. There are individual concrete shelters for the aircraft, dispersed over a large area. Thick layers of concrete protect the operations room and other vital points. The bulk fuel installation is buried and hardened, and split into well-separated parts so that if part of the installation is damaged the aircraft can continue operating. Bomb and missile storage areas are similarly protected. Refuelling vehicles, weapon loading equipment and other items important for the operation of aircraft are dispersed over a wide area.

'The days are long past when one could expect to find enemy aircraft parked on the ground in neat rows. Nowadays all major air forces disperse their aircraft around the airfield in individual hardened shelters which are strong enough to withstand anything but a direct hit or a very near miss from a large bomb.'

From all of this it is clear that a hardened modern airfield is a very difficult target to knock out completely. Nevertheless, if the attack is well planned and the raiders put down sufficient destructive power in exactly the right place, they can halt enemy air operations. With its very accurate aiming system the Tornado can mount toss-bombing attacks on vital installations, such as the fuel and munitions storage areas and headquarters bunkers. And to render the runways unusable the RAF Tornado squadrons have recently received a potent new weapon, the JP233. The Tornado carries two JP233 containers, each shaped like a flattened cigar about 2ft high and 21ft long and holding 30 cratering bombs and 215 small mines.

The JP233 runway-cratering bomb is roughly the size and shape of a roadmender's pneumatic drill without the bit, and weighs about 57lb. As the bomb falls clear of its container a parachute opens to reduce its speed and point the nose towards the ground. When the bomb strikes a runway a small directional charge blows a narrow hole in the concrete, then fires a secondary warhead underneath the runway where it detonates. The force of the explosion from the secondary warhead, confined between the underside of the runway and its foundations, produces a fairly large underground cavity topped with a small hole surrounded by a circle of 'heave' — cracked and broken concrete pushed up from below. If an enemy aircraft tried to take-off over a 'heaved' part of the runway it could damage its undercarriage and might even collapse the weakened layer of concrete and fall into the cavity below. It would require a lot of work to repair the JP233 cavities and bring the runway back into action: before the holes can be filled, the areas of cracked concrete must first be cut away and large amounts of debris removed.

Each Tornado would release 60 such cratering bombs, together with 430 small mines which would end up scattered amongst the rubble and craters to menace the repair teams and delay their work. A typical airfield-attack force might include eight Tornados with JP233, carrying a total of 480 cratering bombs and 3,440 mines. Given sufficient resources, time and determination, the enemy airfield repair teams should be able to bring the runway and taxiways back into use after an attack of this type. But, as Grant McLeod explains, their work would probably not go unhindered.

Right:
A Tornado releasing a load of inert JP233 munitions over a weapons range.

Above left:
An HB876 mine descending by parachute. On striking the ground the parachute is released automatically, and self-erecting feet bring the weapon to the upright position where it will detonate if disturbed. *Hunting*

Above:
Any attempt to clear HB876 mines using a bulldozer would result in a wrecked bulldozer — the warhead of the mine includes a shaped charge designed to pierce the blade and smash the engine of the vehicle. *Hunting*

Left:
A close-up of the empty JP233 containers, after the weapons have been released. The HB876 mines are housed in the front portions of the containers and the SG357 runway cratering bombs in the rear portions.

Below left:
Once empty, the JP233 containers are jettisoned from the aircraft.

'Such attacks would have to be repeated at intervals, and from then on the effect of the damage would be cumulative. If one of our raids caught their damage repair organisation in the open, filling craters from a previous attack, we might be able to destroy their specialised plant — concrete mixers, bulldozers, etc. If that happened we would know that the next time we raided them, they might not have enough plant to repair the damage in a short time and it would take the airfield much longer to recover from such an attack.

'The idea is to damage the airfield, let the enemy begin to repair some of the facilities, then go back later and hit them again. They begin to repair that damage and we hit them yet again. If we could keep that up over a period the condition of the airfield will deteriorate rapidly.'

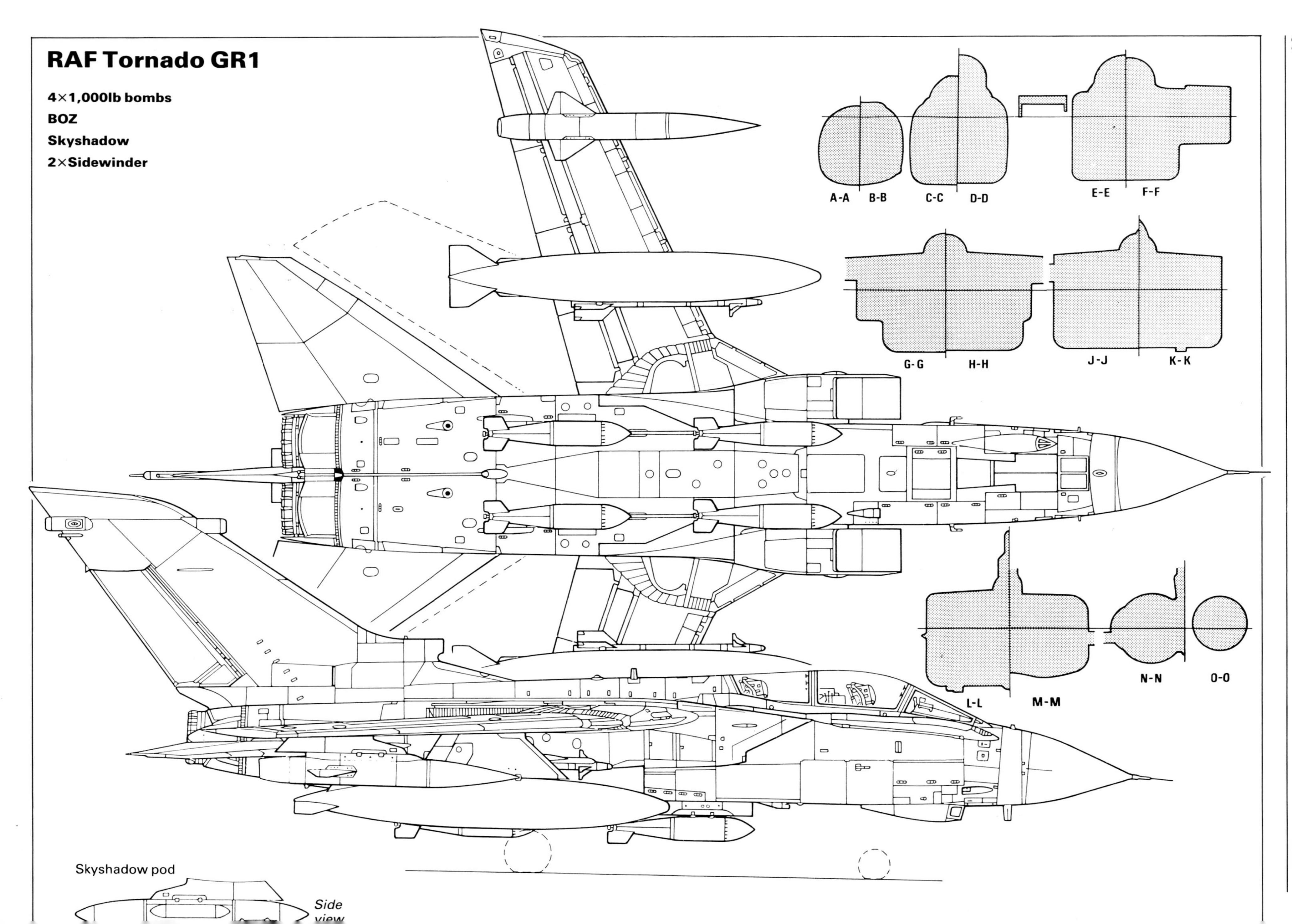

RAF Tornado GR1
4×1,000lb bombs
BOZ
Skyshadow
2×Sidewinder
A-A
B-B
C-C
D-D
E-E
F-F
G-G
H-H
J-J
K-K
L-L
M-M
N-N
O-O
Skyshadow pod
Side view

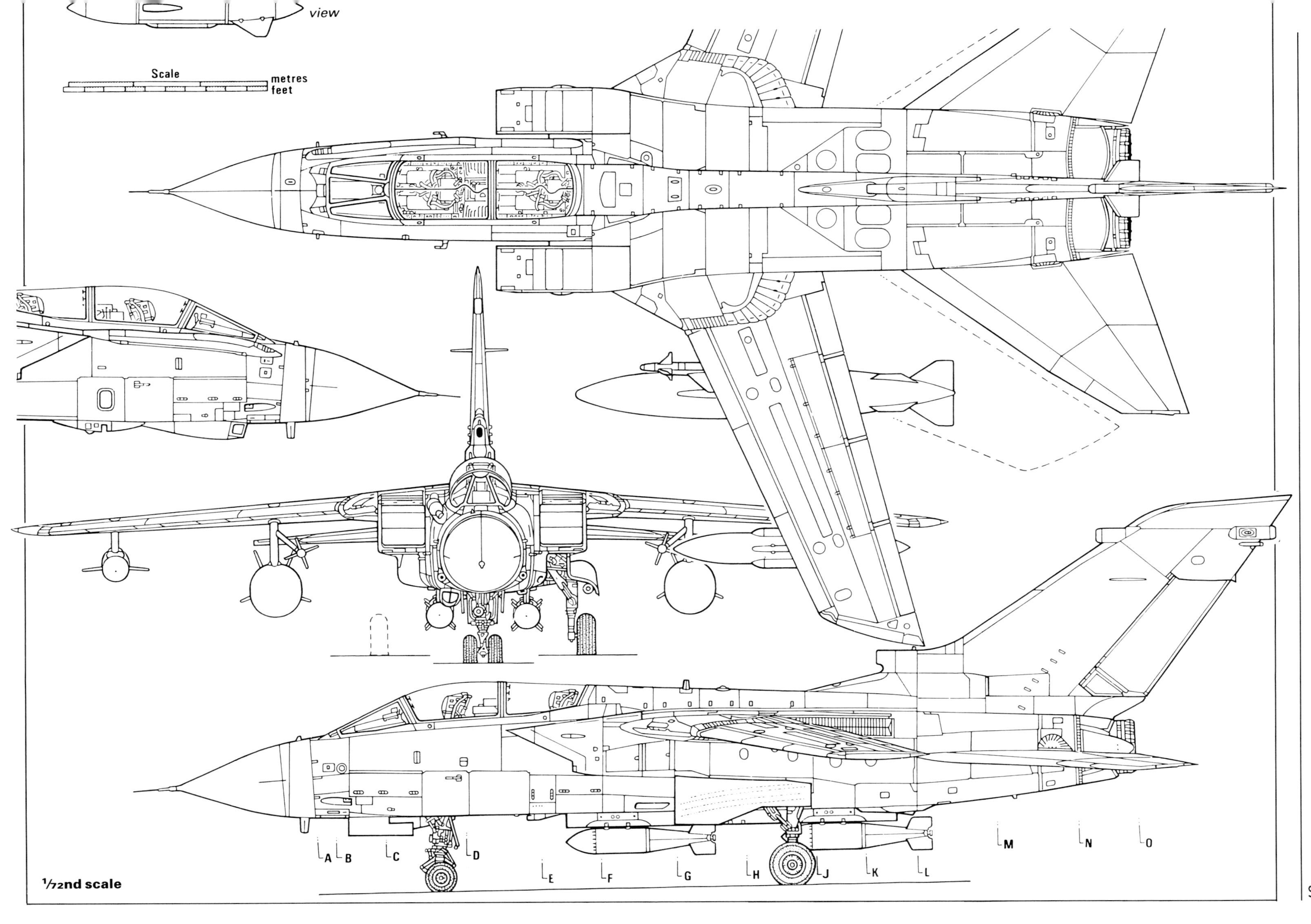
view
Scale
metres
feet
A
B
C
D
E
F
G
H
J
K
L
M
N
O
1/72nd scale

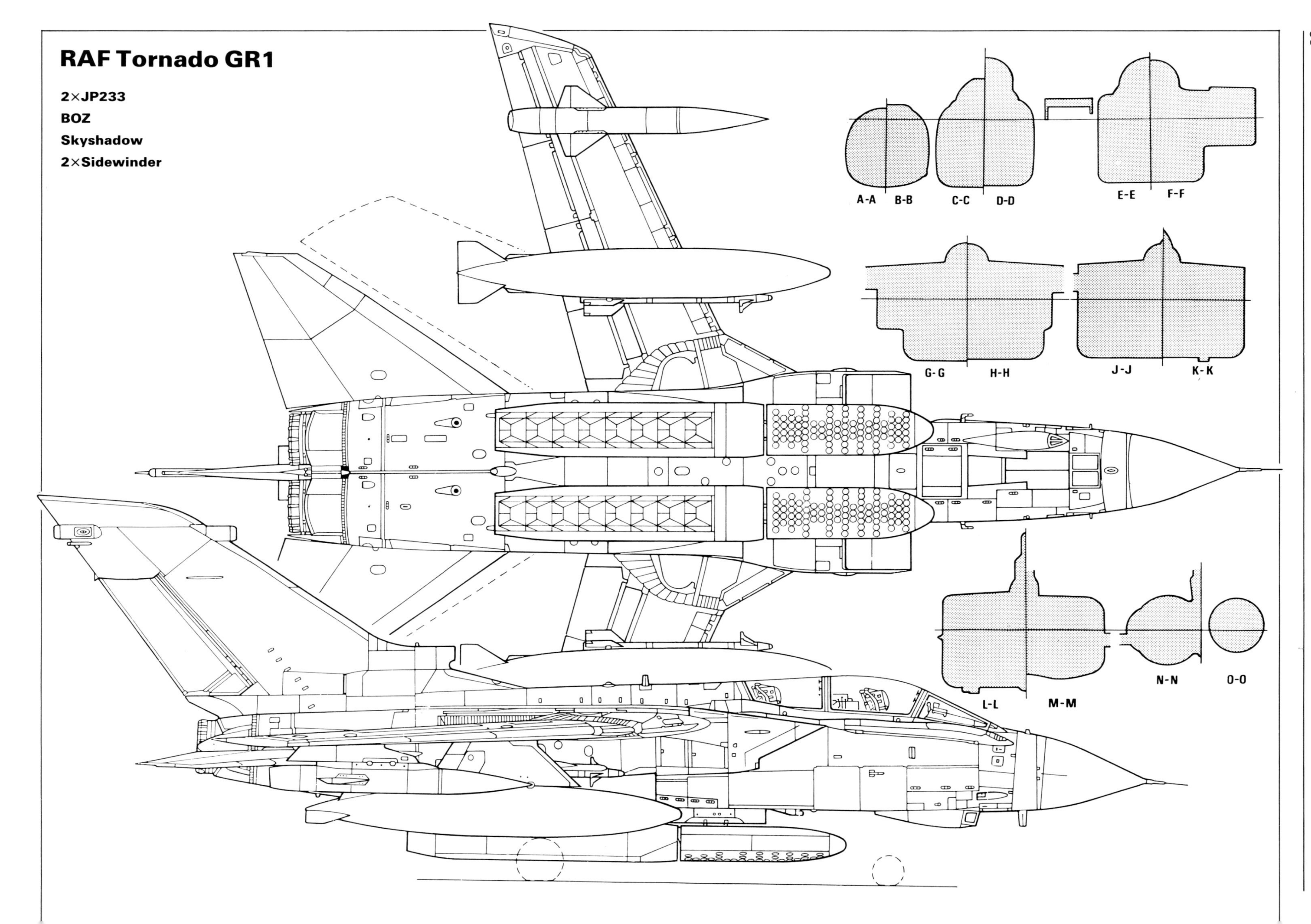

RAF Tornado GR1

2×JP233
BOZ
Skyshadow
2×Sidewinder

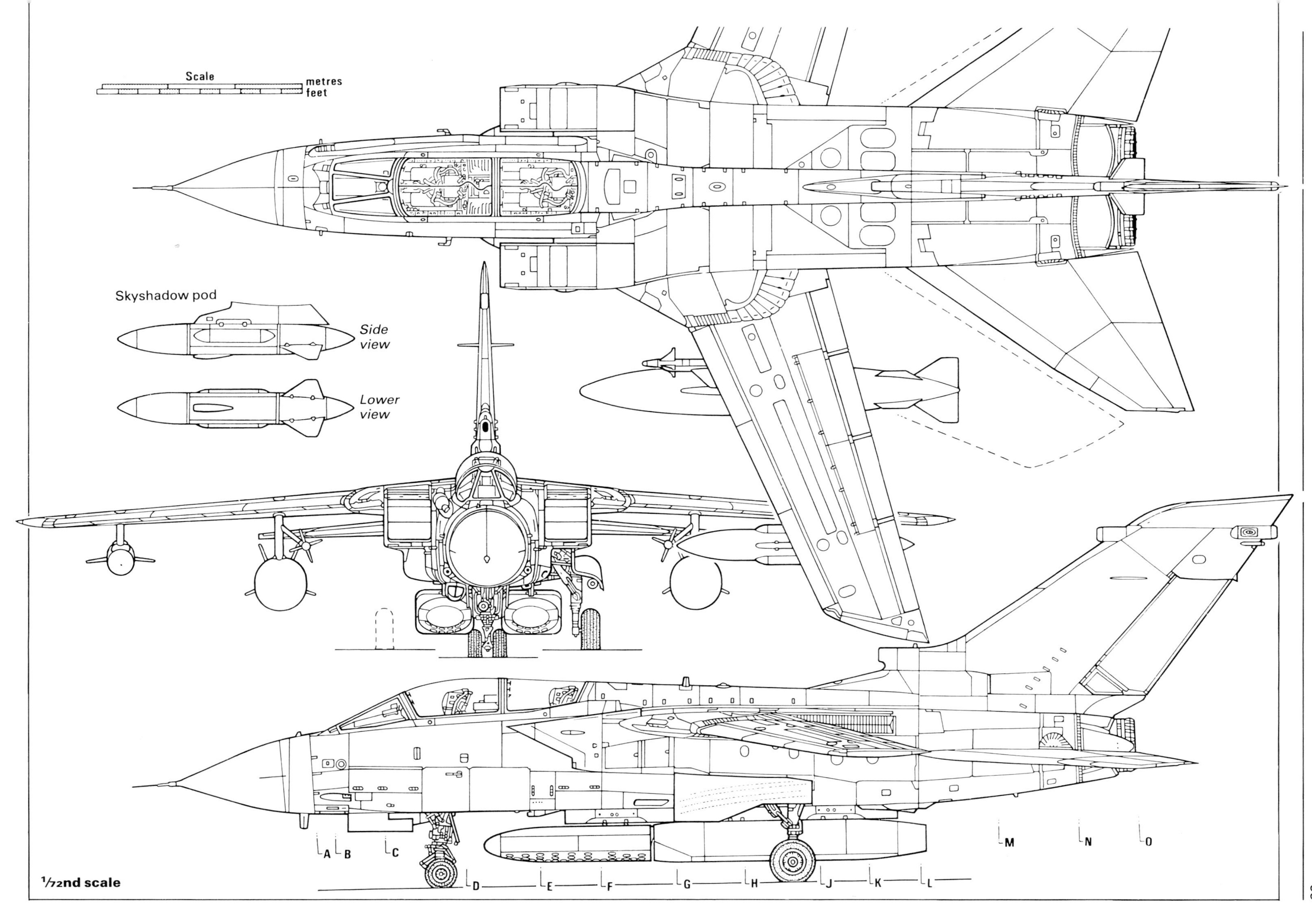
Scale
metres
feet
Skyshadow pod
Side view
Lower view
A
B
C
D
E
F
G
H
J
K
L
M
N
O
1/72nd scale

In Service with the German Navy

The first solely German unit to operate Tornados was the joint Air Force & Navy Weapons Conversion Unit (WaKo), which began forming at Erding near Munich in February 1982 to perform much the same role as the RAF weapons conversion unit at Honington.

The first operational German unit to receive the Tornado was Marine Flieger Geschwader 1 of the Federal German Navy, based at Jagel in Schleswig-Holstein, which received its first aircraft in July 1982 and rapidly built up to its full establishment of 47 aircraft.

The Tornados operated by the German forces are almost identical to the IDS version used by the RAF, except that they have no fuel tank in the fin. In the Germany Navy the aircraft is flown in the maritime role, and in time of war it would conduct reconnaissance and attack missions on enemy shipping in the Baltic and naval facilities on the coast. The main task of MFG 1, and its sister unit MFG 2 (which is re-equipping with Tornados) is to ensure that any amphibious landing operation mounted against northern Germany or Denmark would be an extremely risky undertaking. Fregattenkapitän Volke Liche, the commander of operations of MFG 1, told the author:

'Our task is to attack enemy surface shipping in the Baltic as far east as possible, and the success of such attacks would depend on our getting timely information on the movements of enemy naval forces. The Baltic is a very small area, to an ocean flyer it is like a bathtub. In a time of tension our Breguet Atlantic aircraft would fly

Top right:
Aircraft 43+73 of Marinefliegergeschwader 1 (MFG1) taxies from its dispersal before a mission. This aircraft carries a standard weapon load for attacks on ships in open water: two Kormoran air-to-surface missiles under the centre fuselage, two drop tanks and two AIM-9 Sidewinder missiles on the inner wing pylons, BOZ pod under the port wing and Cerberus pod under the starboard wing.

Centre right:
A close-up of a Cerberus electronic jamming pod fitted to a Tornado of MFG1. This equipment is standard on all operational Tornados of the German Air Force and Navy, and the Italian Air Force.

Right:
A close-up of a BOZ-100 chaff and infra-red decoy dispensing pod on a Tornado of MFG1. This pod is standard equipment on all operational IDS Tornados of the Royal Air Force, the German and Italian Air Forces and the German Navy.

Above:
Tornados of MFG1 of the German Navy in their element, flying over the Baltic.

continuous reconnaissance missions over the Baltic, but once the shooting started these slow aircraft would be unable to operate in that area and our Tornados would have to take over the reconnaissance task.

'Operating in the long range reconnaissance role, Tornados would fly without offensive armament, carrying two drop tanks under the fuselage in addition to the two normally carried under the wings. With four tanks the Tornado has an endurance of about four hours, sufficient to take along the Baltic as far east as Leningrad — more than 750 nautical miles from Jagel if the aircraft stays over the sea.'

When flying such reconnaissance missions the Tornados would fly singly at low altitude. They would use radar only intermittently to search for shipping, the rest of the time remaining radar-silent to conceal their positions.

When operating in the anti-shipping role the German Navy Tornados would normally carry two Kormoran anti-ship missiles under the fuselage, and two drop tanks, two Sidewinder air-to-air missiles and two ECM pods under the wings. The German-built Kormoran operates in much the same way as the air-launched Exocet which caught the world's attention during the Falklands conflict in 1982. The missile carries a 364lb warhead, weighs 1,300lb at launch and has a maximum range of about 20 nautical miles. Before launch the Weapon Systems Officer (or WSO, as Tornado back-seaters are known in the German and Italian air arms) feeds the position of the target ship into the missile and once it is launched the Kormoran is on its own; in modern parlance it is a fire-and-forget weapon. The self-contained navigation system guides the missile to the target area, then the missile's radar is switched on and searches for the target. The radar locks itself on to the largest radar echo within its angle of view and guides the missile towards it, skimming low over the sea at near-sonic speed until impact.

Right:
Test firing a Kormoran missile from a Tornado of MFG1.

Below:
Final moments of the flight of a Kormoran, aimed at a de-commissioned German destroyer. Kormoran is a sea-skimmer, similar in operation to the Exocet missile which achieved prominence during the Falklands conflict.

Right:
Damage inflicted by the Kormoran, sufficient to put a warship out of action for a considerable time.

MFG 1 Tornado crews are trained to attack ships with 1,000lb, 500lb and 250lb bombs, both ballistic and retarded, and BL755 cluster bombs. Their primary anti-ship weapon is the Kormoran.

For an attack on an enemy naval force the Tornados would usually operate in six-aircraft attack flights. On nearing the enemy naval force the Tornado formation would split up and aircraft would move individually to their missile launch positions in accordance with a prearranged plan. The aim would be to launch the first salvo of missiles simultaneously, so that they would converge on the target force from several different directions and achieve maximum surprise, concentration and shock effect.

'With its very exact navigation system the Tornado can fly to a given point precisely, to within less than a second. So we can arrange for all of the aircraft to arrive at assigned points at exactly the same time. The idea is for the aircraft to launch their missiles simultaneously from many different directions, to saturate the defences around the enemy force.'

As well as providing a most difficult problem for the defenders, having the aircraft launch their attacks from separate assigned sectors prevents them getting in each others' way during missile launch, and it reduces the chances of two or more aircraft attacking the same ship.

During the final moments of such an attack, things would happen very quickly.

'The Tornados would run in singly towards their assigned missile launch points, keeping below the enemy radar cover. We would use the Kormoran's stand-off capability to its fullest extent and fire the missiles at their maximum possible range. When the WSO estimated his aircraft was within Kormoran range of the target he would switch on his radar and the enemy force should appear on his screen. If it did not, the pilot might have to climb the aircraft a little until the ships did appear.'

Above:
For extended-range operations German Navy Tornados can employ the Sargent Fletcher 'Buddy Buddy' refuelling system. The aircraft plugged into the tanker carries the standard two Kormoran attack load and features the new wrap around camouflage scheme applied to German Navy Tornados. The aircraft nearest the camera carries five 1,000lb low-drag bombs under the fuselage in place of the Kormorans, an effective load for use against ships in harbour or for finishing off ships previously hit and put out of action by Kormoran.

Having selected his first target the WSO would place an electronic marker over its blip on the radar screen, press a button to lock the target into the attack computer, then launch the first missile. Several seconds after launching its first missile each aircraft would launch its second, then turn tightly through a semi-circle and withdraw at high speed. Provided the Tornados kept more than 10 miles from the escorting warships and stayed low, they would be safe from enemy surface-to-air missiles. To guide a missile on to an aircraft and knock it down, a ship's missile operators would need to be able to lock their fire-control radar on to the aircraft for at least a minute (the missile would need much of that time to cover the distance). Normally the Tornados would not expose themselves above the radar horizon for anything like that length of time.

The time of flight of a Kormoran missile, from launch at maximum range to impact, is about two minutes. Throughout this time the enemy convoy would be in the thoroughly discomforting position of having a dozen missiles streaking towards it at low altitude and high speed, from several points on the compass. Even though some of the ships might be able to deflect missiles using electronic countermeasures, there is a high probability that several of the missiles would score hits. Any ship hit by a Kormoran would probably be immobilised and have its fire control radars knocked out, and could be finished off in a later attack with 'dumb' bombs.

The recent conflict in the South Atlantic brought to the fore the effectiveness of air-launched sea-skimming missiles against surface ships. Did Volke Liche feel the conflict held any lessons for the German naval air attack units?

'The lessons from the Falklands War are for the surface warships rather than for us. The success of the Argentine air-launched Exocets has convinced people that in Kormoran we have the right sort of weapon, but we in the Marine Flieger Geschwader knew that before the conflict. The people on our surface ships, they learned a lot from the British experience. During our German national exercises, and NATO exercises, we gave our surface warships the opportunity to try to counter our type of attack. The handling of surface ships, their sea-skimming missile defence procedures and tactics, have improved quite a bit.'

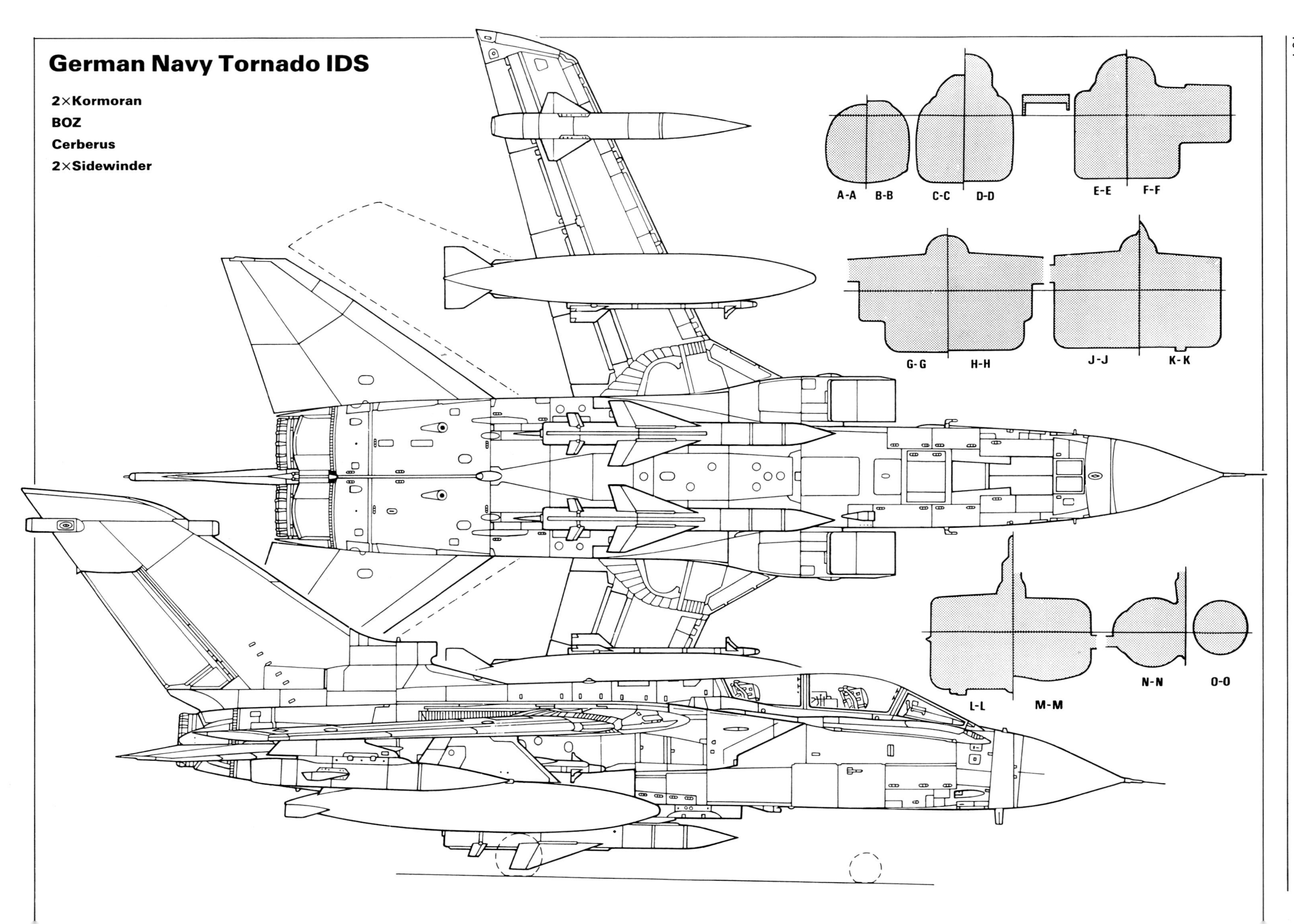
German Navy Tornado IDS
2×Kormoran
BOZ
Cerberus
2×Sidewinder
A-A
B-B
C-C
D-D
E-E
F-F
G-G
H-H
J-J
K-K
L-L
M-M
N-N
O-O

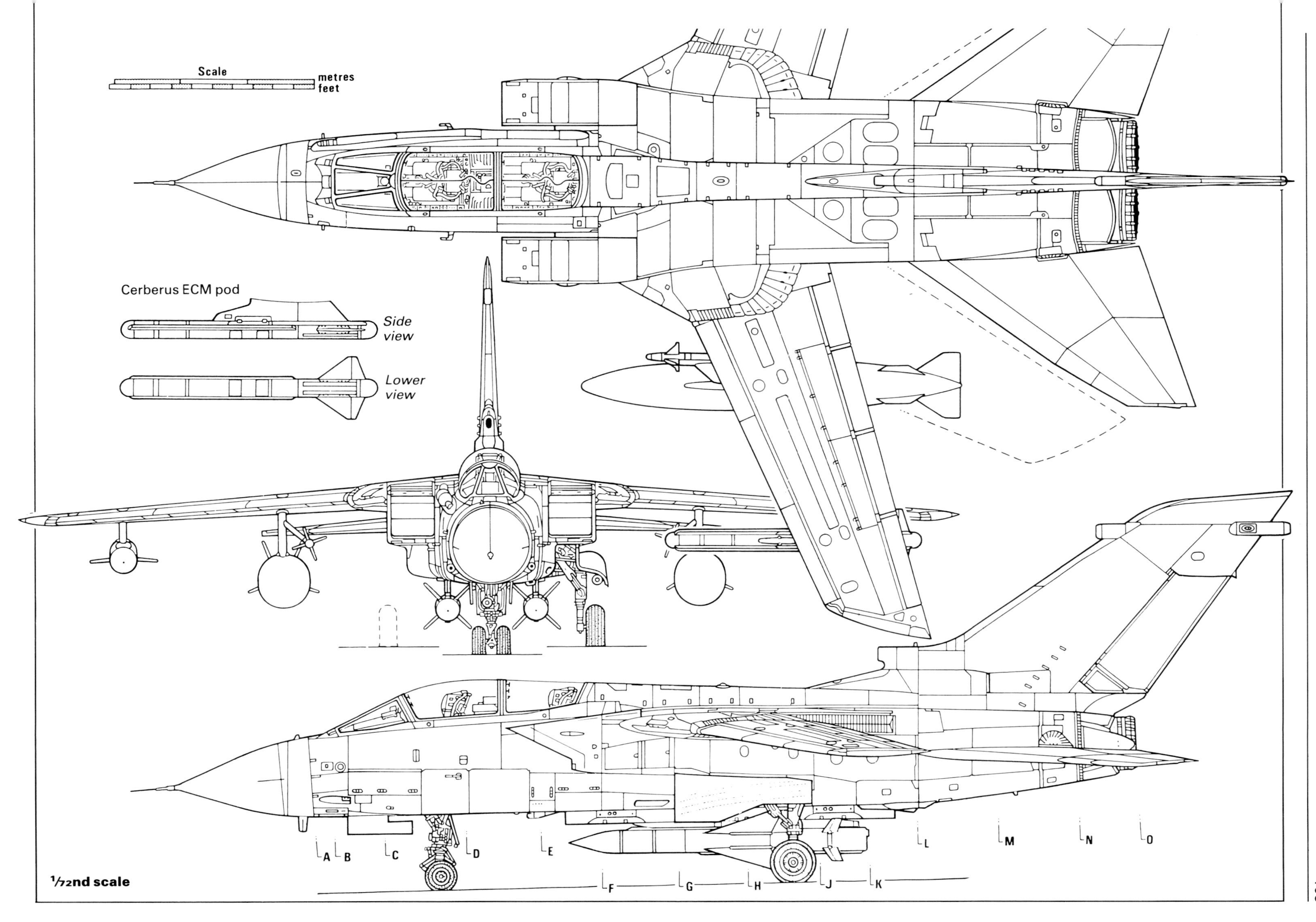
Scale
metres
feet
Cerberus ECM pod
Side view
Lower view
A
B
C
D
E
F
G
H
J
K
L
M
N
O
1/72nd scale

In Service with the German Air Force

The first operational unit in the German Air Force to receive Tornados, in August 1983, was Jagdbombergeschwader 31 based at Noervenich near Cologne. The unit comprises two Staffeln and has an established strength of 38 aircraft. Next was Jagdbombergeschwader 38 based at Jever in Ostfriesland, formed early in 1984 from aircraft and crews of the Weapons Conversion Unit at Erding; JaboG 38 retained the earlier unit's commitment to provide weapons training for all new German Air Force and Navy Tornado crews. In August 1984 Jagdbombergeschwader 32 based at Lechfeld in Bavaria became the third German Air Force Geschwader to re-equip with Tornados, followed by JaboG 33 at Büchel and JaboG 34 at Memmingen.

Originally the German Air Force had to be talked into taking an aircraft with the range and carrying capability necessary for the deep interdiction and offensive counter-air missions. Once that service had accepted the potential of this type of mission, and with the zealousness of converts anxious to prove their new faith, the Germans squeezed the concept for all it was worth. Taking the long flat underfuselage of the Tornado as a starting point, the MBB company designed a huge weapons container to fit under it. The resultant system, the MW-1, is slightly longer than a Volvo estate wagon with the width and depth of an average-sized kitchen table. A range of specialised sub-munitions has been developed for use with MW-1, and currently three types of load are in service in the German Air Force: about 4,500 armour-piercing bomblets, for use against tanks and armoured vehicles; about 650 fragmentation bomblets, for use against troops and soft-skinned targets; and with a mixed load of about 2,250 anti-tank bomblets and 500 anti-tank mines to bring enemy armoured units to a halt (in each case exact figures on the numbers of bomblets are classified). Other types of sub-munition are under development, including a runway cratering weapon similar to that used by JP233. The weight of a MW-1 container varies with the type of sub-munitions carried, but is about 4½ tons.

To scatter such a large number of sub-munitions evenly over the target area, the MW-1 employs a novel method of dispensing. The sub-munitions are housed in packs, in 112 horizontal tubes each 132mm (5.2in) in diameter running the width of the main container at right angles to the aircraft's line of flight. The sub-munitions are loaded on either side of an explosive charge in the centre of each tube. When detonated, the charge fires the packs of sub-munitions away from each other and out the sides of the container, so that each load cancels out the recoil force from the other. The largest charge will fire the sub-munitions approximately 250yd from the aircraft, to give the pattern of bomblets a maximum width of 500yd. By using a range of different explosive charges, and firing them at brief intervals in a set order controlled by a computer, the MW-1 distributes its sub-munitions fairly evenly throughout the pattern on the ground.

The density of the MW-1 bomb pattern depends on the type of sub-munition used. The highest density pattern is used during attacks on tanks or armoured vehicles, when the armour-piercing bomblets need to score direct hits on the hulls of the vehicles to knock them out. Against a concentration of such targets the MW-1 would be programmed to fire all 4,500 anti-tank bomblets in just over half-a-second, to cover an area of approximately 500yd by 180yd — about twice the length and twice the width of a football field. This gives an average of one bomblet per 20sq yd — the approximate area of a battle tank — and would inflict hits on a very high proportion of vehicles within the area of the bomb pattern.

When used to attack soft-skinned vehicles or troops, the fragmentation bomblets have a much greater radius of effectiveness than armour-piercing bomblets. Therefore, a much lower density of bomblets is necessary and they can be spread over a greater area by increasing the time intervals between firings, thus increasing the length of the bomb carpet.

Immediately before an attack with MW-1 the crew must release the underwing drop tanks, otherwise some of the sub-munitions would smash into them. Apart from restricting the aircraft to a maximum speed of 600kt, the huge MW-1 container has remarkably little effect on the Tornado's handling characteristics. Oberstleutnant Walther Jertz, head of operations of Jagdbombergeschwader 31, told the author:

'Fully loaded the MW-1 container weighs approximately 4½ tons, but it does not make much difference to the handling of the aircraft because the Tornado's computer-controlled stability

Facing page: top to bottom, left to right:
Test firing MW-1 anti-tank munitions from 98+03, the 16th and final pre-production Tornado. Once clear of the aircraft the cylindrical bundles break up into seven KB-44 armour piercing bomblets (top far right). MW-1 can put down its full load of some 4,500 KB-44 bomblets evenly over an area twice the length and twice the width of a football field, with a density sufficient to score hits on a high proportion of any vehicles in that area. Alternatively, the MW-1 can be loaded with a small number of MUSA bombs for use against soft-skinned targets (centre far right) or MIFF mines for area denial (bottom far right).

Right:
Aircraft 44+32 of Jagdbombergeschwader 31, the first operational unit to receive Tornados, carrying an MW-1 weapons container. During operational missions the aircraft would usually carry a drop tank on the inner wing pylons, but these would have to be jettisoned before the attack or the laterally fired MW-1 munitions would strike the tanks.

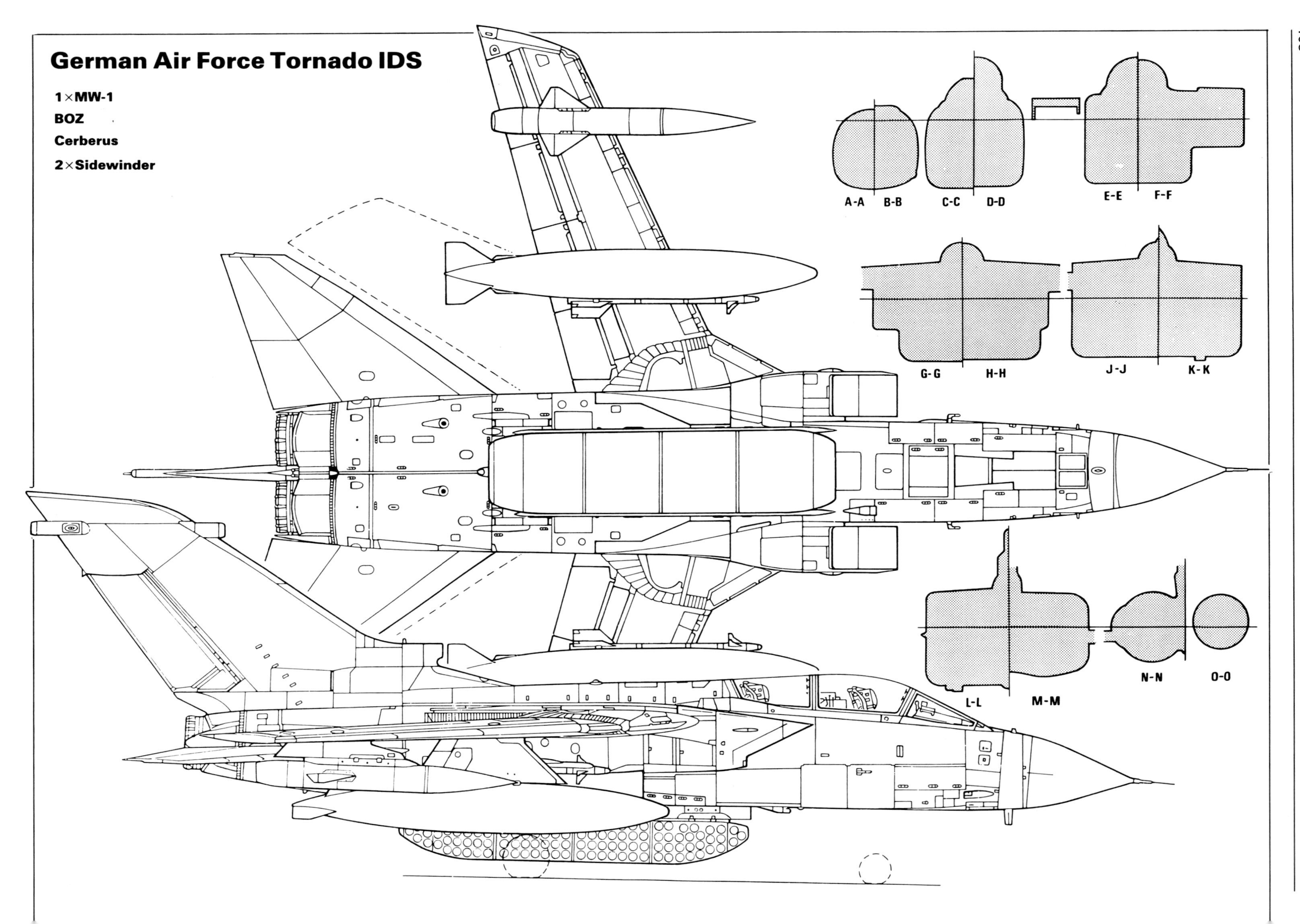
German Air Force Tornado IDS
1×MW-1
BOZ
Cerberus
2×Sidewinder
A-A
B-B
C-C
D-D
E-E
F-F
G-G
H-H
J-J
K-K
L-L
M-M
N-N
O-O

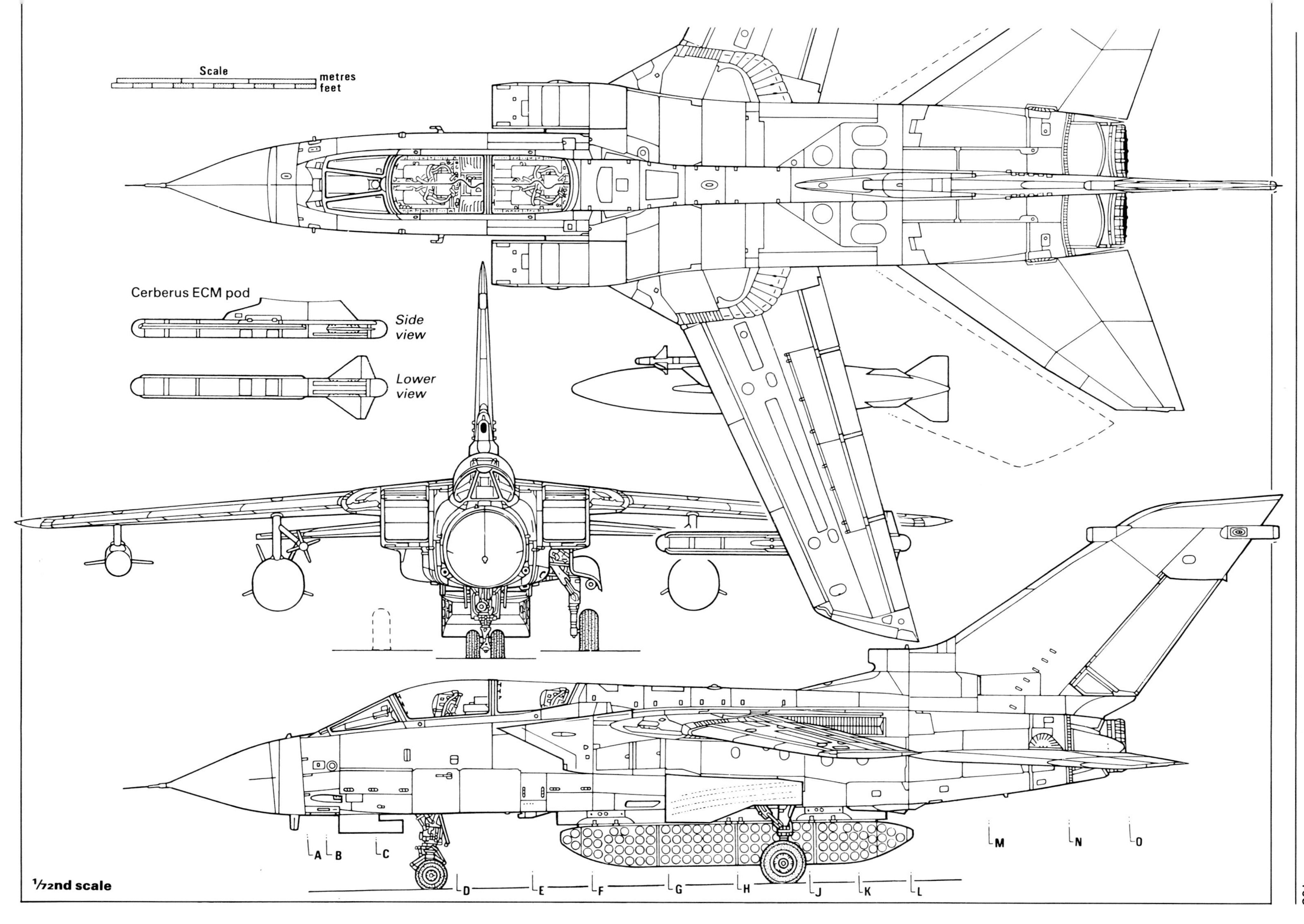
Scale
metres
feet
Cerberus ECM pod
Side view
Lower view
A
B
C
D
E
F
G
H
J
K
L
M
N
O
1/72nd scale

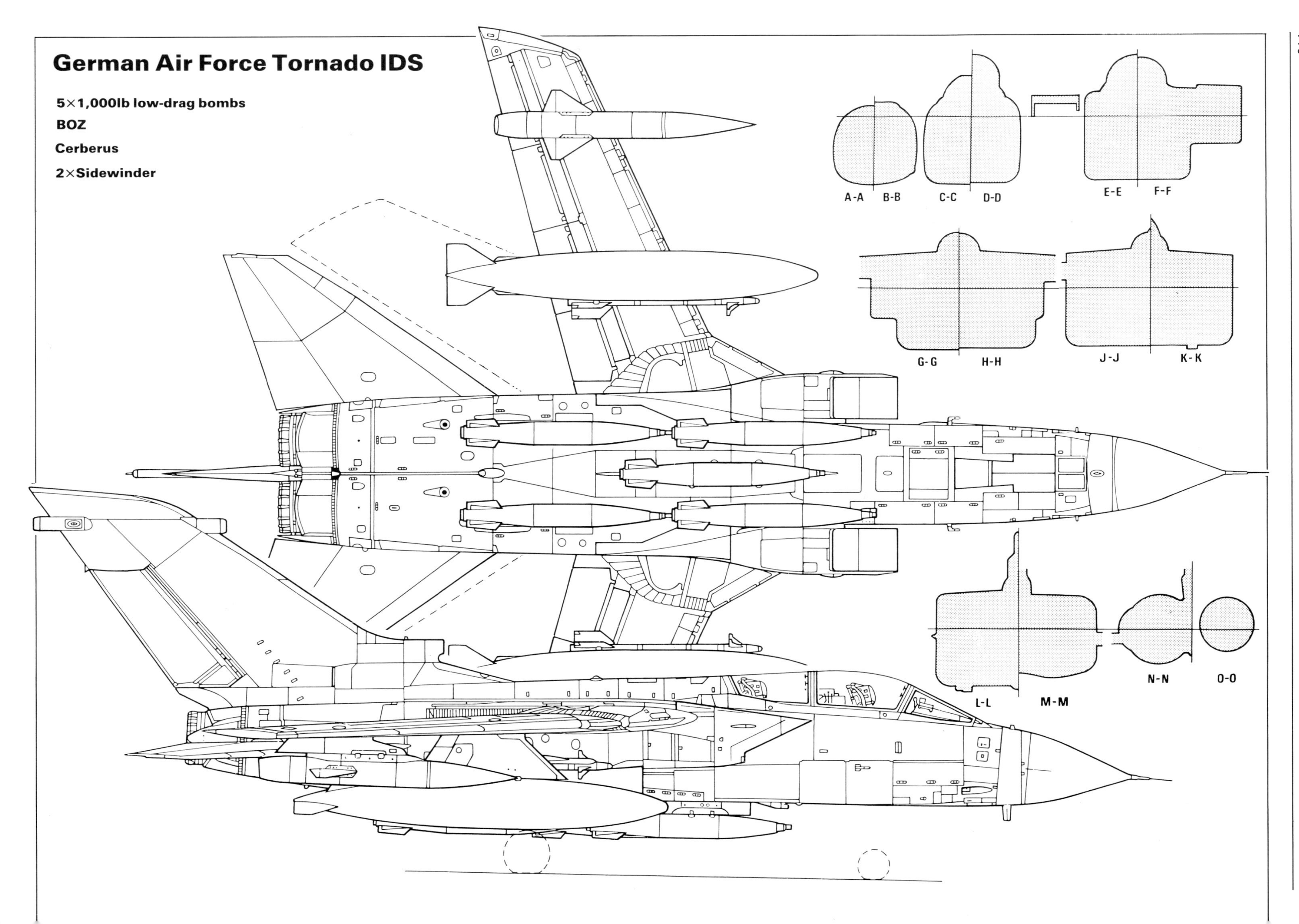
German Air Force Tornado IDS
5×1,000lb low-drag bombs
BOZ
Cerberus
2×Sidewinder
A-A
B-B
C-C
D-D
E-E
F-F
G-G
H-H
J-J
K-K
L-L
M-M
N-N
O-O

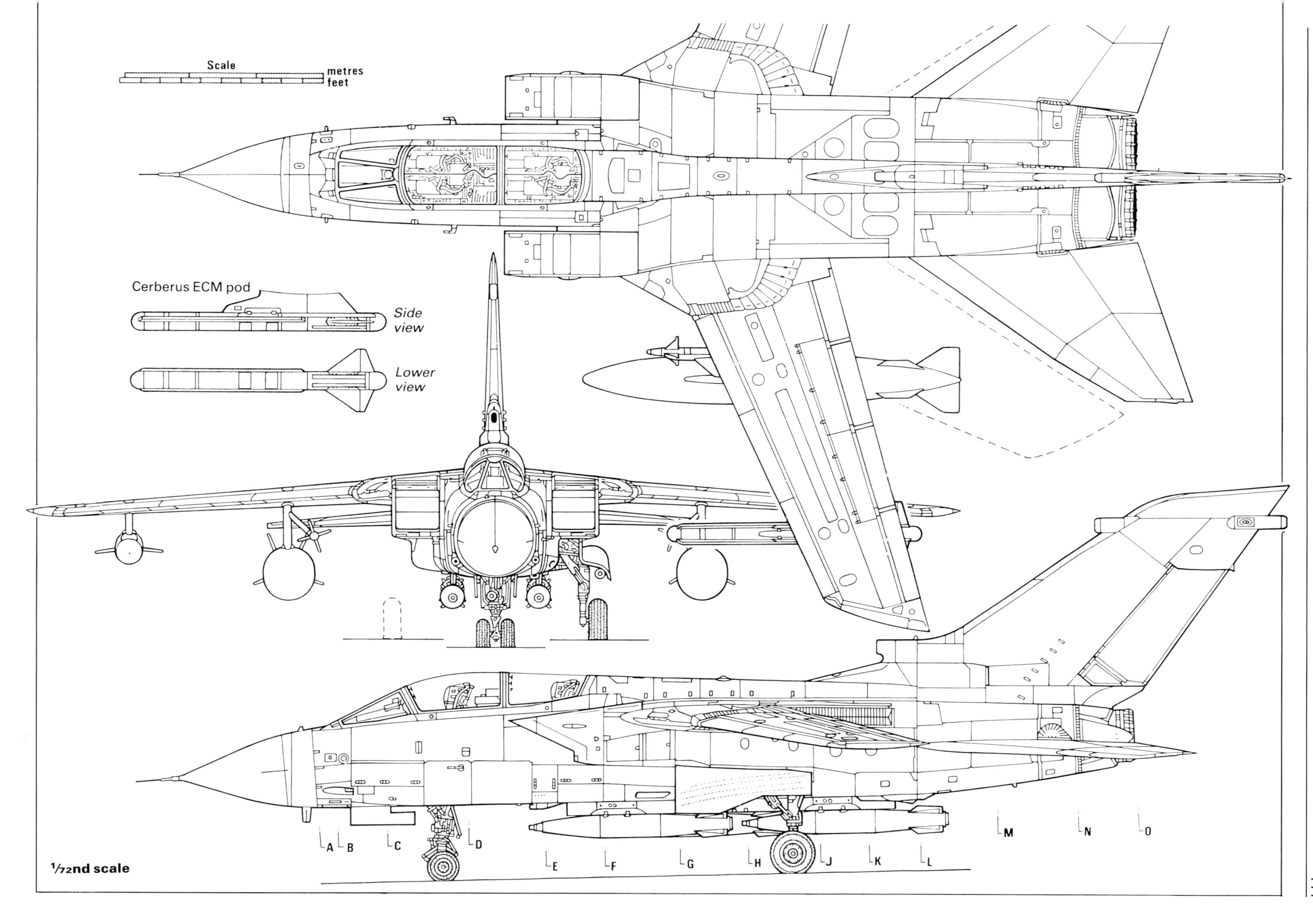
Scale
metres
feet
Cerberus ECM pod
Side view
Lower view
A
B
C
D
E
F
G
H
J
K
L
M
N
O
1/72nd scale

Below:
Groundcrewmen loading the rear of the four sections of the MW-1 container on a Tornado.

Bottom:
A German Air Force ground crewman using a borescope to check the turbine blades of the port RB199 of a Tornado. After 150 hours flying the blades are checked after each additional five hours flying, and provided no sign of damage is detected the engine continues in use.

augmentation system is able to adjust for it. The normal tactics for use with MW-1 are to fly over the target at more than 500kt at 150ft to lay down the pattern of sub-munitions. When the MW-1 container is empty it is jettisoned.

'An ideal target for MW-1 is a concentration of vehicles, attacked at night or in bad weather when they don't expect us. Because we can fight at night when their troops would be moving up, we could be very dangerous to the enemy.'

When sent to engage an enemy column at night the Tornados would usually fly in units of two or four aircraft.

'When making for the target area at night or in poor weather we would observe the old German military adage ''*getrennt marschieren, vereint schlagen*'' [split up for the march, concentrate for the attack]. So aircraft would fly singly, and come together at the target.

'Using its computerised system the Tornado is able to navigate to designated points exactly, plus or minus zero seconds. Typically we would fly two aircraft in front and two a few miles behind, a maximum of four on the same route using what we call parallel tracking: pairs of aircraft flying one mile to either side of that common track to make sure they do not hit each other. In that way the aircraft can fly in formation without having to see each other or break radio silence.'

During their penetration of the enemy defences Tornados would normally fly with their wings swept back at 45° to give a good turning performance at low altitude. When passing through defended areas or if threatened by enemy fighters, the pilots would select maximum wing sweep and accelerate.

'The normal cruising speed for the Tornado is 450kt, increased to go through the FLOT [forward line of own troops]. Once past the FLOT we would throttle back to a speed which gives the best compromise between the requirements of survivability on the one hand, and fuel consumption and therefore combat range on the other. If I was intercepted by an enemy fighter I would accelerate to 600kt and put my wings fully back to 67°. A Tornado flying at 200ft at that speed at night or in poor visibility is very difficult for a fighter to catch.'

Once the drop tanks and the empty MW-1 container have been jettisoned, an almost 'clean' Tornado is fully capable of supersonic speed at low altitude should this be necessary.

As well as MW-1 the German Air Force Tornado units are equipped with the usual range of general purpose bombs — 1,000lb, 500lb and 250lb, both retarded and unretarded — and BL755 cluster bombs.

The MW-1 is a devastatingly effective weapon, but having a means to destroy a concentration of enemy vehicles is only half the battle: first the concentration has to be located, and information on the whereabouts of moving vehicles

Above:
Tornados of the 154° Gruppo of the 6° Stormo, the first Italian Air Force unit to receive Tornados. This unit is based at Ghedi near Brescia in the north of the country.

becomes 'stale' very quickly. It could take two hours for a conventional reconnaissance aircraft to return from the scene, its crew be debriefed, and the attacking crews receive their briefing and get airborne. That is far too long: in that time an enemy armoured division on its way to the front could move 20 miles or more. The answer, as the German Air Force sees it, is to operate some Tornados as 'attack leaders': these are specialised reconnaissance aircraft with infra-red sensors to enable them to locate lucrative targets in enemy territory for formations of attack aircraft following, say, 5-10min behind. Having located a target, the reconnaissance aircraft will radio the position to the follow-up aircraft. As the attacking force approaches the target the reconnaissance aircraft will operate in the 'Wild Weasel' defence suppression role, using its in-built electronic sensors to locate enemy missile control radars in the area and engage them with HARM radiation-homing missiles. Initially the German Air Force wanted 40 or more new-build electronic combat & reconnaissance (ECR) versions of the Tornado, but the requirement has been pared down to 35 aircraft.

In Service with the Italian Air Force

The first Italian Air Force unit to form with Tornados was the 154° Gruppo of the 6° Stormo, based at Ghedi near Lake Garda, which received the first of its establishment of 18 aircraft in August 1982. Next to re-equip was the 156° Gruppo of the 36° Stormo at Gioia del Colle near Bari in the south, followed by the 155° Gruppo of the 51° Stormo, based at Treviso.

Italy does not border on any nation belonging to the Warsaw Pact, and in time of war its Air Force's main roles would be to support operations in Austria or Yugoslavia if either nation came under attack from Warsaw Pact forces, and to engage enemy shipping in the Mediterranean in support of the Italian Navy. The Italian Air Force operates its Tornados in a less specialised way than the RAF or the German Air Force or Navy. Generale da Brigatta Lorenzo Gioru, commander of the 1st Air Region (which includes all Italian Air Force units based in northern Italy), explained to the author the reasons for this:

'The main roles for the Tornado in our Air Force are nuclear strike, conventional interdiction and ground attack, and anti-ship operations. The philosophy of our air force is that the Tornado has no specialised role, we have to use to the full the flexibility which the aircraft gives us. We have few aircraft, so we need to use them in the most effective way. Pilots are trained to fly nuclear strike, attack and anti-ship missions.

'Later we will have some aircraft fitted out for reconnaissance. The Tornado will give us a much better tactical reconnaissance capability than the F-104 it will replace. With the F-104 the Italian Air Force had specialised reconnaissance squadrons. But now our philosophy is to regard the reconnaissance pod as just another type of armament, which can be put on the aircraft or taken off as required. That will give our Tornado squadrons dual reconnaissance and attack roles.'

The main types of non-nuclear attack weapon carried by the Italian Air Force Tornados are American 1,000lb and 500lb bombs, BL755 cluster bombs and Kormoran missiles. MW-1 dispensers and American Maverick electro-optical homing missiles are on order.

Generale Gioru discussed the anti-ship mission as it applies to his Tornados:

'The Italian Air Force is responsible for providing air cover for the Italian fleet. We have done a lot of practice deployments to the south of Italy and to Sardinia to train in the anti-ship attack role. All of our Tornados have provision to carry Kormoran and we have the missiles. We train in night attacks against ships using tactics similar to those used by the German Navy. We have close contact with them. Our tactical area for anti-ship operations is almost the entire length of the Mediterranean, approximately from the Balearic Islands to Crete.'

To increase the operational radius of action for the anti-ship role, Italian Tornados can be fitted with the American Sergeant Fletcher buddy-buddy pod for passing fuel to other aircraft. The Italian Air Force is actively considering the purchase of specialised tanker aircraft to support the Tornado force.

In the Italian Air Force, as in other services, the Tornado has provided a major challenge to the ground crews. Tenentecolonelo (Wing Commander) Paolo Baroni, the senior engineering officer at Ghedi, explains:

'With the Tornado we introduced a new maintenance philosophy and that gave us some problems. With the F-104 we used the concept of planned maintenance: we inspected the aircraft at the end of each 25 hours' flying, and certain "lifed" equipment items were replaced. The more difficult tasks took place when the aircraft went into the hangar for second-line servicing.

'In contrast the Tornado has "on condition" maintenance for most items; that' means components are inspected, and changed only if they are found to be faulty. We still have some "lifed" items — certain engine parts, components of the flying controls and electrical items — but far less than on the F-104. For example, on the F-104 we had to do an engine change after each 400 hours flying. With the Tornado, after 150 hours flying the turbine blades are checked after each subsequent five hours flying, and if the blades look all right the engine continues to fly. If some of the blades are found to be damaged only the turbine module of the engine need be replaced, we don't need to change the entire engine.'

The Tornado's electronic systems are contained in some 650 Line Replacement Units (LRUs), which greatly eases the task of the ground crews. Baroni continues:

'Another good feature of the Tornado is the concept of the LRU. If we change parts of the avionic system, no calibration or alignment of the sensors is necessary. On the F-104, after changing part of the inertial navigation system, it was necessary to do a full calibration of the system in the aircraft and that took about eight hours. If we change part of the inertial navigation system in the Tornado, it is a simple matter of changing LRUs and no further calibration is necessary. On the Tornado we can even change the complete nose radar without having to calibrate it.'

To be fully effective the LRU system requires a goodly supply of spare units, however, and during the early stages of the Tornado's service career these were not always available. The position has since improved.

Below:
A Tornado of the 155° Gruppo, 36° Stormo, the second Italian Tornado unit, which is based at Gioia del Colle near Bari in the south of the country.

8 The Tornado Squares For the Fight

With the longer and slimmer nose giving it a more rakish look than the attack version, the first prototype Tornado ADV made its maiden flight from Warton on 27 October 1979. The second prototype joined the test programme in July 1980.

The new variant of the Tornado had 80% commonality with the IDS version of the aircraft, but the 20% difference — confined mainly, but not exclusively, within the fuselage forward of the air intakes — gave it the different set of capabilities necessary for the new role. The 21¼in long extension plug inserted in the fuselage just forward of the air intakes, necessary to provide room under the fuselage for the specified load of four Sky Flash missiles, also provided room for an additional internal fuel tank with a capacity of 200gal. To house the greater volume of avionics necessary for the long-range air defence role — about one half again more than in the IDS version — the length of the nose forward of the cockpit was increased by a further 32½in; overall, therefore, the ADV is just over 4ft 5in longer than the IDS version. The ADV carries no terrain-following radar, so the nose cone covering the single scanner of the Marconi AI24 Foxhunter multi-mode radar is somewhat slimmer than that fitted to the IDS version. To make room for the fully retractable flight refuelling probe on the port side of the nose, the 27mm cannon was omitted on that side and the aircraft carries only one of these weapons.

The flight testing of the new variant moved ahead rapidly and by the summer of 1980 its flight clearance envelope had been extended to 800kt (indicated), faster than most fixed geometry aircraft at low altitude and much faster than any aircraft carrying an external bomb load.

During the second half of 1984, production Tornado F2s began to leave the assembly line at Warton and in November the first pair arrived at No 229 Operational Conversion Unit at Coningsby. The AI24 Foxhunter radar built for the aircraft by Marconi Defence Systems had run into severe production and performance problems, and until some of these had been sorted out the Royal Air Force refused to accept production sets. Accordingly the first ADVs delivered to the service carried ballast in place of the radar; such deficiencies are not uncommon when a new type of aircraft first enters service, but in the case of the Tornado that ballast would have a disconcerting longevity.

By July 1985 No 229 OCU had received nine of its establishment of 16 Tornado F2s. The Foxhunter radar was still not working to specification, but production sets worked well enough for a few to be installed in the aircraft so that full crew training could begin. At Coningsby there was a repeat of the process at Cottesmore when the first IDS versions arrived, as the unit strived to build up its total of flying hours and train its complement of pilot and navigator instructors.

At the time of writing the Foxhunter radar is still not working to specification. Many Tornado ADVs still carry ballast in place of this most essential piece of equipment, on which the fighter's operational effectiveness depends to a crucial extent. Marconi are making strenuous efforts to overcome the radar's problems. Should they fail, there have even been hints that the Foxhunter might be replaced by a derivative of the Hughes APG-65 radar fitted to the F-18 Hornet.

The Tornado F2 was the interim production version of the new fighter fitted with Mk 103 engines and launchers for only two Sidewinders; only 18 examples were built. The definitive version of the fighter is the F3 with Mk 104 engines which give increased thrust in reheat at all altitudes; the F3 has automatically controlled wing sweep, twice as much computer power as the F2, launchers for four Sidewinders, and several other detailed improvements compared with the initial production version. It is planned later to retrofit some of these improvements to the F2s, making them into F2As, and No 229 OCU had all its F2s replaced by F3s by the end of January 1987. The first operational squadron to receive the new fighter was No 29 Squadron based at Coningsby, receiving Tornado F3s to replace its Phantoms in 1987; between then and 1991 six other squadrons belonging to No 11 Group are earmarked to receive F3s.

In an earlier chapter Grant McLeod described the progression in capability he had seen over four generations of RAF ground attack aircraft, the Hunter, the Phantom, the Jaguar and the Tornado. Wg Cdr Rick Peacock-Edwards, Commander of No 229 OCU, described in similar terms the progression he had seen over four generations of Royal Air Force aircraft operating in the air-to-air fighting role: the Hunter, Lightning, Phantom and Tornado:

'The Hunter was a clear air mass day fighter, with a good dogfighting capa-

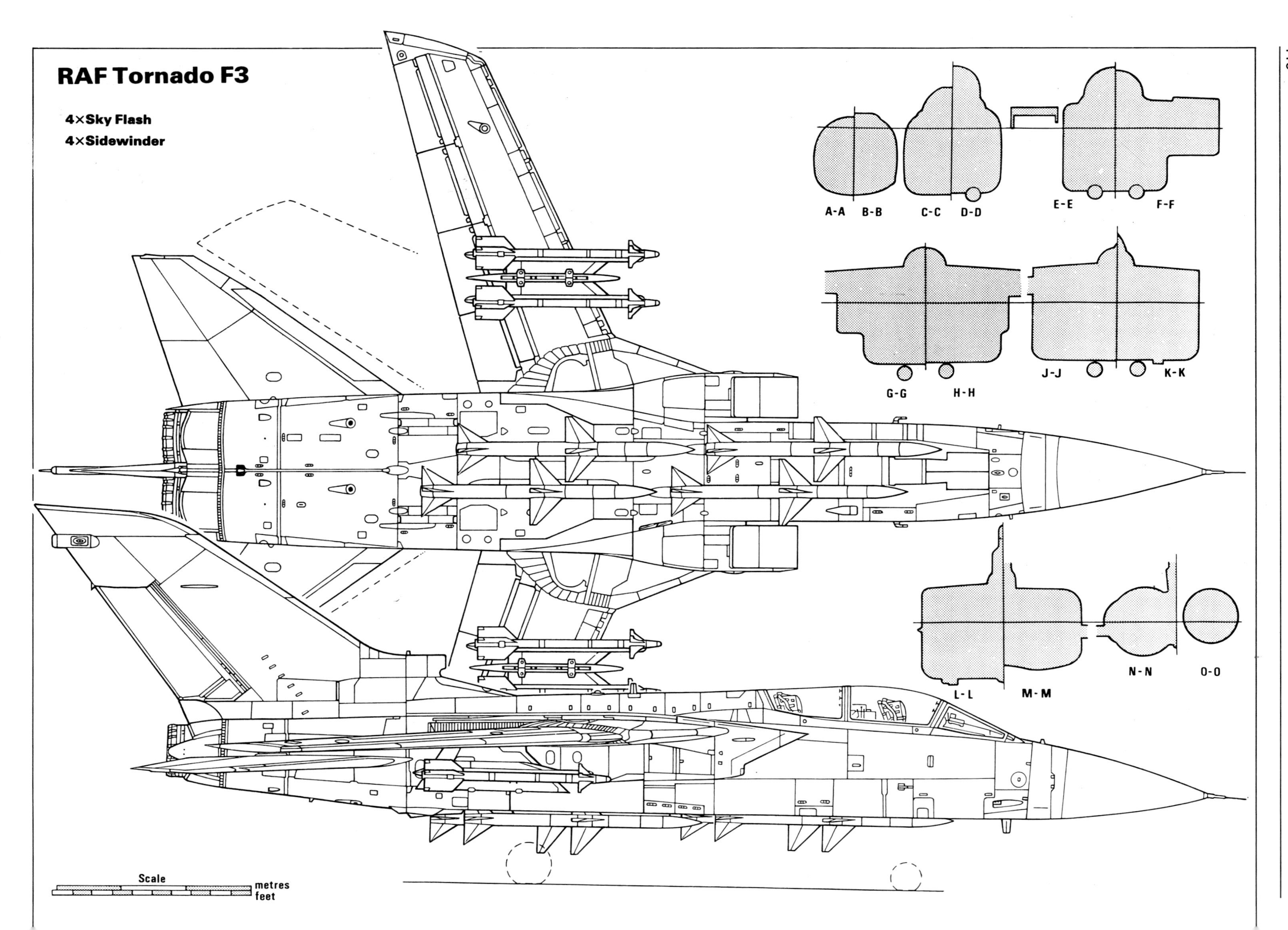
RAF Tornado F3
4×Sky Flash
4×Sidewinder
A-A
B-B
C-C
D-D
E-E
F-F
G-G
H-H
J-J
K-K
L-L
M-M
N-N
O-O
Scale
metres
feet

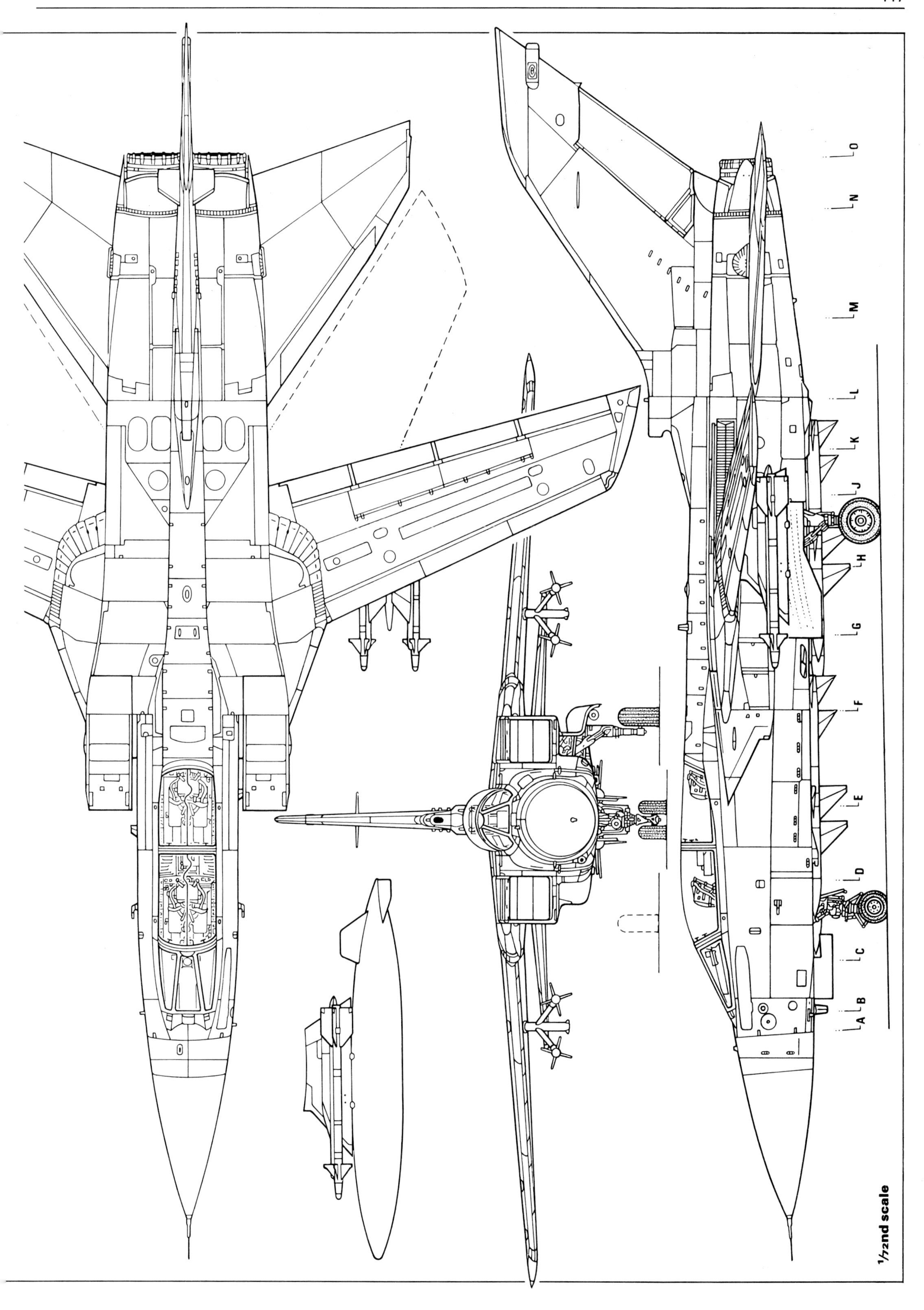
A
B
C
D
E
F
G
H
J
K
L
M
N
O
1/72nd scale

bility with guns; but it had no missile capability, no search radar, no computer to assist with navigation. For its time it was a superb day fighter but that was all it was.

'Compared with the Hunter, the Lightning was a much faster and more effective quick reaction interceptor. It could intercept targets further from base and it could be refuelled in flight, which gave a much better endurance. It carried a search radar and missiles so it had a night and all-weather capability. But the radar did not have a "look down" capability, so against low-flying aircraft it was very limited. The Lightnings which I flew carried Firestreak, which was a first-generation infra-red homing missile of limited capability. As a high-level fighter the Lightning was — and still is — jolly good. Its speed and acceleration are as good as the Tornado's, though it cannot turn as well as the Tornado — the Tornado is a much better turner at all speeds.

'The Phantom gave a major leap in capability compared with the Lightning. Carrying two or three tanks the Phantom's range and time on patrol, unrefuelled, were far superior to those of the Lightning. In a Lightning the average sortie without refuelling was about an hour, in a Phantom it was about 2½ hours. Also the Phantom had the increased capability that came with a two-man crew. It had greatly improved avionics; in particular the radar was vastly better than the Lightning's: in the Lightning the detection range on a large aircraft like a "Bear" [Tupolev 95] was about 30 to 40 miles; in the Phantom we could pick up "Bears" at 90 to 100 miles. Operating in the pulse-Doppler mode the Phantom's radar and missiles have a very good look-down shoot-down capability.'

At the time of writing, all RAF Phantoms operate in the interceptor role and carry four Sky Flash radar semi-active missiles, four AIM-9L Sidewinders and sometimes a 20mm cannon pod under the fuselage.

'The mixed weapons load carried by the Phantom is very useful, giving it a very much better fire power than the Lightning had. The Sky Flash radar-homing missiles give the fighter a good long-range head-on engagement capability. The Sidewinder heat-seeking missiles give a good capability close-in to the target.'

On a cursory glance at the brochure performance figures of the Tornado F3, it might seem that the new fighter offers little advance over the Phantom it is to replace. At high altitude the new fighter is little faster than its predecessor; and at the time of writing both the Phantom and the F3 carry the same missile armament. In fact, the Phantom is still an extremely effective fighter in the long-range interception role for which the Royal Air Force uses it, and one of the few things to be said against the older fighter is that the airframes and engines are starting to wear out and will need replacing at the end of the decade. However, when assessing the fighting value of the Tornado compared with its predecessor, yardsticks other than brochure performance have to be applied. For the late 1980s a fighter defending the UK requires a high maximum speed *at low altitude*, a long endurance and a radar able to pick up small targets — such as cruise missiles — at great distances. Once the problems with the radar are sorted out, the Tornado F3 should be a considerable improvement over the Phantom. Although its airframe is somewhat smaller than the Phantom's, this version of the Tornado carries almost the same internal fuel though in cruising flight its engines consume one-third less. This enables the new fighter to fly most types of mission without external tanks, and that helps its fuel go even further: with no external tanks the Tornado F3 can achieve supersonic speed in a short dive without resort to reheat, a valuable factor should it need to fight a protracted high speed engagement. In high speed combat external fuel tanks can be

Top:
The first Tornado ADV pictured at Warton, before painting.

Above:
The roll-out ceremony of the first Tornado ADV, ZA254, is August 1979.

Above right:
ZA254 pictured during or soon after its maiden flight.

Right:
A fine pair of air-to-air shots of ZA283, the third ADV to fly. Protruding from the leading edge of the fin near the top is a cine camera, one of the non-standard items of equipment fitted to this aircraft.

a liability: to sustain supersonic speed the pilot has to use reheat, and a lot of extra fuel is burned because higher power settings are necessary to overcome the drag of the tanks themselves. Tornado F3s need to carry underwing tanks only during ferry flights or patrols exceptionally far from base (in marked contrast to most other combat aircraft types, which would be ineffective on combat sorties without at least one external tank). The new fighter has other advantages over its predecessors, as Rick Peacock-Edwards explains:

'The Lightning and the Phantom were both 1950s technology fighters. The Tornado ADV is a 1975 technology aircraft and you can feel the difference. The Tornado ADV gives a far more comfortable fighting environment than in the Phantom, the cockpit is much quieter, visibility is far better and the handling of the aircraft is much nicer.

'The Tornado is primarily a bomber-destroyer but it has a good dogfight capability, it can take on enemy fighters if it has to. With the wings forward it is a good turning aircraft. But if the pilot gets himself into a difficult situation in a dogfight and wants to "bug out" quickly, he can put the wings back to 67° and open the throttles, and the aircraft will accelerate very rapidly. The Tornado has the capability to go very fast or, if the pilot wants to, it can go very slow.

'The Tornado ADV was designed for the long-range interception role, and there is no doubt it is able to do that very well. It can go out a long way and loiter, it is very fuel efficient in dry power [ie not in reheat]. Even when "clean" the Tornado has an endurance of three hours, which is as long as a Phantom carrying tanks can fly without refuelling. Put tanks on a Tornado and it can spend a very long time on patrol a great distance from base.'

The Tornado F3's various modern features have given its pilots a whole lot of new capabilities. When it works to its specified capability, the aircraft's AI radar promises to enable navigators to direct interceptions on a series of targets. Sqn Ldr Andy Lister-Tomlinson, a navigator instructor on No 229 OCU with considerable previous experience on Phantoms, told the author:

'In the Phantom we had to rely on an analogue computer to process the raw data from the radar. The Tornado uses digital computers which are much faster, more versatile and more accurate. If there were several aircraft on the screen, the Phantom radar operator had to look at the radar blips moving across his screen and try to work out in his head what each of the aircraft was doing; if he wanted to know their rates of closure he had to lock the radar on each one in turn. In the Tornado we can designate to the computer those targets we are interested in, ask it to track those targets and it simultaneously works out the targets' headings, their speeds, heights and closure rates and it builds up a track history on each. As a result the navigator is able to come up with a series of interception solutions much faster than was possible in the Phantom.'

The new fighter is on the threshold of its service career and there are two important systems in the development stage which could substantially increase the new aircraft's fighting effectiveness: AMRAAM and JTIDS.

At the time of writing the RAF intends to replace Sky Flash on Tornado F2s and F3s with the American-designed AMRAAM (AIM-120 Advanced Medium Range Air to Air Missile). The earlier missile employs radar semi-active homing; in other words, the attacking aircraft locks its radar on the target aircraft, and the missile homes on signals reflected from the target. The big disadvantage of this method during a long-range engagement is that the fighter has to maintain radar lock from missile launch to missile impact, which in an extreme case could be as long as a minute. During that period the fighter cannot engage any other enemy aircraft with its long-range missiles, and during a head-on attack the closing speed will be such that there will rarely be time to engage more than one target before the fighter reaches the enemy formation.

In contrast, AMRAAM can be used to engage several targets simultaneously, and the weapon carries its own active terminal homing system for use during the final part of the interception. Obviously, a Tornado carrying four

Above:
Delivery of the first two Tornado F2s, ZD901 and ZD903, to No 229 Operational Conversion Unit, Coningsby, in November 1984.

AMRAAM would be considerably more effective than one carrying four Sky Flash; with the newer missile the fighter could engage enemy aircraft at long range in rapid succession, without having to complete each engagement before it launches the next missile. The advantages AMRAAM could give the Tornado F3 in combat are clear enough. But they will depend on the effective solution of two major but separate problems: firstly, AMRAAM has to be made to work reliably and at a reasonable cost; and secondly the crew will need to be confident that the aircraft they are engaging so effectively at long range do in fact belong to the enemy.

It has been difficult to squeeze the required capabilities into the relatively small AMRAAM airframe, and its designers have had to draw heavily on the latest technology. The development of the missile has taken far longer than expected, and it has been dogged by problems of reliability and large cost overruns. In 1986 the predicted price for 17,000 AMRAAMs was $5.4 billion — more than $300,000 each. Yet there is a danger that if it goes into production, AMRAAM will exceed even this high unit cost, and the future of the missile is far from assured.

JTIDS (pronounced Jay-Tids, Joint Tactical Information Distribution System), scheduled for introduction in NATO tactical aircraft during the 1990s, is a technically elegant but extremely complex data link system for passing air defence related information rapidly between ground stations and aircraft. JTIDS will produce on one of the TV-type screens in the Tornado a plan position display showing the whereabouts of all friendly aircraft and known hostile machines, over an area which might be as large as a fighter Group's area of responsibility during the Battle of Britain. Used in combination with the Tornado's air-to-air IFF interrogation system, and a new radar homing warning receiver able to identify aircraft by analysing the signals coming from their radars, JTIDS should be of great assistance in establishing the identity of aircraft detected on radar. Like Foxhunter and AMRAAM, JTIDS has run into difficulties which have delayed its entry into service, though almost certainly several Tornados will be carrying it by the mid-1990s.

The Tornado F3 is fast enough, manoeuvrable enough and has a good enough radius of action for the UK air defence task well beyond the year 2000. And it is large enough to accommodate improved weaponry and air defence avionics as they become available. The Royal Air Force has staked a great deal on the new fighter being able to fulfil the all-important home defence task. If the teething problems of its AI radar, JTIDS and AMRAAM can be overcome, or if it is fitted with replacement systems which circumvent these difficulties, there is little doubt that the Tornado ADV will take its place amongst the most formidable fighters in the world.

9 Overview

In August 1985 the Omani Government signed a contract with Panavia for the purchase of eight Tornado ADVs. Although small, the export order marked a significant breakthrough for the tri-national programme: not only was this the first order from a nation outside the original partnership, but it was the first order for additional Tornados since the signing in 1976 of the Memorandum of Understanding to put the aircraft into production. In September 1985 the Saudi Arabian Government announced its intention to buy 72 Tornados, 48 IDS versions and 24 ADVs. Early in 1986 the RAF placed an order for nine more IDS aircraft. Shortly after that the German Air Force signed a contract for 35 examples of the projected electronic combat and reconnaissance variant.

Added to the 10 prototypes, two pre-production series aircraft and 809 production aircraft previously ordered, the new contacts bring the total order for Tornados to 945 at the time of writing.

That the Tornado reached operational service is, in itself, a major success for the tri-national programme. The aircraft survived because the harsh penalty clauses in the international agreement made it too expensive for any one government to pull out of the programme once it started moving. It is a fact that in a democratic country there will be changes of government from time to time and new sets of political priorities; and this will probably happen at least once during the 10 years or so it takes to develop a major combat aircraft and bring it into service. Since such a development programme will devour a significant part of even a medium-sized nation's defence budget, and since in the short term cancellation is a relatively painless political option, it is hardly surprising that so few national aircraft-building programmes have survived in Europe in recent years. Any discussion of the relative merits of a national programme to produce a combat aircraft in Britain, Germany or Italy (or any European nation except France or Sweden), compared with a multi-national programme, must take into account the high risk of cancellation of the former; against this background, suggestions that a national programme might produce an aircraft closer related to the needs of an individual air force, or one that is cheaper or available sooner, tend to be irrelevant.

Surprisingly, senior British, German and Italian Air Force officers do not resent the fact that the aircraft their services have in the mid-1980s is so markedly different from the one each had asked for in the 1960s. Discussing the Tornado programme as Assistant Chief of Air Staff, Air Vice Marshal Tony Skingsley told the author:

'One could argue that the Tornado GR1 is a better combat aircraft than it would have been had we in Britain built it as a national strike/attack aircraft. The TSR2 was optimised as a weapon carrier which could fly fast and accurately at low level. The Tornado has the same capability, but because it has a swing wing and some of the other countries wanted a better air-to-air performance, it has a lot more power than we in the RAF would have asked for in the interdiction role. The Canadians had a particularly high requirement for specific excess power; they later withdrew from the project and the requirement was brought down. But the Germans and the Italians were stronger on this than we were and as a result the aircraft now has a very good specific excess power.

'In 1968 the RAF did not require the aircraft to have a real short take-off and landing capability; that requirement came from the Germans whose airfields are nearer to Warsaw Pact forces. Now I am very glad the Tornado has this capability, because we are concerned about what an enemy might do to our airfields if he has a weapon like JP233. I am very glad Tornado has the short take-off and landing performance it has; but initially it was not a British requirement, it was something we gained.'

At first glance this might suggest that in the 1960s the RAF had made a mess of its operational requirement, but this was not the case. In a democracy, a fighting service has to equip itself to fulfil the commitments decided by its nation's politicians, and since then Britain's foreign policy has changed considerably. No longer must the RAF maintain forces equipped for operations outside Europe; and now an attack aircraft with a very large radius of action without refuelling, though always desirable, is no longer essential. During the same period the German and Italian air arms have become much more confident in their application of air power and more wide-ranging in their outlook; senior officers from both nations have expressed to this author their appreciation that the RAF pushed for the additional range, the two-man crew and the more sophisticated avionic systems which make the Tornado a far more capable aircraft than their predecessors had wanted. In other

Above:
Breakthrough: pictured taking off from Warton are the initial pair of 72 Tornados ordered for the Royal Saudi Arabian Air Force. They were the first of these aircraft purchased by a country outside the tri-national partnership.

words, as a result of an unforeseen chain of events over a decade and a half, the RAF's range requirement has fallen while German and Italian air arms have learned the advantages of having a medium-range precision attack aircraft with a night and all-weather capability. The result, in the mid-1980s, is that the partner nations' perceived requirements are far closer to what the Tornado is able to provide than appeared to be the case when the aircraft was originally conceived.

The Tornado programme had demonstrated that the three European nations could work together as equal partners, to build a major combat aircraft to rival any comparable machine in the world. Measured against all criteria short of actual war, the Tornado has shown itself to be a highly effective combat aircraft in most of its intended roles. When fitted with the weaponry and equipment appropriate to the role, the Tornado can perform the interdiction, offensive counter-air, anti-ship, long-range bomber destroyer and reconnaissance roles as well as, or better than, any other aircraft currently in service. The dual control version is perfectly adequate as a conversion trainer for pilots learning to fly the aircraft. The Tornado can mount effective close air support missions against concentrations of enemy vehicles in the battle area; for example if there is a breakthrough and the army commander needs to delay the enemy advance while he moves troops into blocking positions. Also the Tornado *could* attack enemy vehicles dispersed in the battle area though this would be a misuse of an expensive machine — rather like driving a Rolls-Royce Corniche through heavy traffic to the corner shop for a packet of cigarettes.

Of the roles for which the Tornado was originally designed, the only one in which it is unlikely to see use if there is a conflict in Europe is that of air superiority: seeking out and engaging enemy high performance fighters in turning fights at altitudes of *their* choosing. Any Tornado ADV which allows itself to be drawn into a high altitude dogfight with one of the latest Soviet types, the Sukhoi 27 'Flanker' or the MiG 29 'Fulcrum', could be in for a very thin time. If the ADV could engage the enemy fighters on *its* terms, below 10,000ft, it would probably have the edge; but to expect to do so regularly would presuppose a degree of co-operation from the enemy which probably would not be forthcoming in time of war. If handled properly, the Tornado ADV should have little difficulty in dealing with the less-modern enemy fighter types.

In assessing the importance of the Tornado in the NATO order of battle, it has to be seen in the context of air operations over central Europe or its seaward flanks. NATO's air forces operate a range of aircraft types whose performance characteristics and weaponry would define their main roles in time of war. F-104s, F-4s, F-15s, F-16s and F-18s would fly air-superiority missions over continental Europe. F-111s would mount attacks on the more distant airfields and interdiction targets. British, German and Italian Tornado IDS aircraft would attack the less distant airfield and interdiction targets. Harriers, NF-5s, Mirages, F-16s and Alphajets would mount shallow interdiction attacks and some close air support missions. A-10s would fly close air support missions. Army anti-tank helicopters would engage enemy armoured units which had broken through the main defensive line. Appropriately equipped Tornados, Harriers, F-16s, Mirages, Alphajets, RF-4s and Jaguars would fly tactical reconnaissance missions. On NATO's seaward flanks, German Navy and Italian Air Force Tornados, RAF Buccaneers and US Navy A-6s and A-7s would deliver attacks on enemy shipping. Tornado ADVs and F-4s would provide long-range air defence for the UK and with USN F-14s and F-18s would provide cover for shipping in the surrounding sea areas. That would be the general pattern of air operations, though commanders would not adhere to it rigidly, for flexibility always has been the key to the effective use of air power. It can be seen that in any major war there would be plenty of targets for Tornados operating in their main roles; and there would be plenty of other types able to take on the close air support and air superiority roles for which the Tornado is not the best aircraft available.

Considering the inherently hazardous nature of high speed flight at low altitude, the Tornado has proved comparatively reliable and safe in service. Up to October 1987, 25 Tornados had been lost in accidents. Many people will argue that there is no acceptable aircraft accident rate as such, just as there is no acceptable road accident rate; but if an air force trains hard in peacetime there will be accidents, and a lower rate is always better than a higher one. The Tornado's overall losses include those in the aircraft's flight test programme, and is commendably low for a combat aircraft operating in such a role. Certainly, the Tornado's accident record is vastly better than that of its predecessor in the German Air Force and Navy attack units, the F-104 Starfighter: 91 German Starfighters crashed during a six-year period

Left:
A Tornado of the Royal Saudi Arabian Air Force shows off its desert camouflage.

between 1962 and 1968, and that excludes those lost in the USA during the aircraft's flight test programme.

Of the Tornado accidents only three have been attributed to failures of the aircraft. The first, already described, resulted from a total failure of the aircraft's electrical system. The second took place in July 1984 when a German Air Force Tornado on a low altitude sortie flew within two miles of the Radio Free Europe transmitter near Munich and suddenly dived into the ground; there is clear evidence that the powerful radio signals had induced spurious commands into the aircraft's electronic flying control system. Tornado crews now have strict orders to give such broadcast transmitters a wider berth. Following these two crashes the relevant aircraft systems were modified, and there has been no recurrence of either type of accident.

The third such loss occurred in March 1987, when an RAF Tornado based at Brüggen crashed following an unspecified 'mechanical failure'; both crewmen ejected safely.

The Tornado is a successful combat aircraft, it is relatively safe and reliable in operation and considering its technical complexity it has gone into service with remarkably few teething troubles. But it would be misleading to suggest the programme has not had its negative aspects. Of these, the most serious is the inordinate length of time the aircraft took to reach service. It has been said that development of the Tornado has moved at the pace of a glacier, and compared with most American aircraft construction programmes that is a fair comment. It took 65 months from the start of the definition phase of the new aircraft to its first flight (the equivalent period for the F-111, which was a larger and for its time rather more innovative aircraft, was 25 months); from the first flight of the MRCA until the first Tornados entered service was 71 months (for the F-111 it was 39 months). Much of the slowness in developing Tornado stemmed directly from the tri-national management of the programme. Considerable time was spent arguing out each aspect of the design of the aircraft, though in Brian Young's view this did produce one substantial advantage:

'There was a tendency for everybody to want to say his piece, or if he had an idea to chuck it into the pot. Because of this the total technical effort for a collaborative project is significantly higher than the technical effort for a single nation project. Figures like 1.7 or 2 have been bandied around for the additional effort for the total design activity. That certainly increased the initial development cost. On the other hand there are clear advantages of having opposite or different viewpoints during the design stage; you look into things rather more deeply and the technical quality of the aeroplane benefits.'

It is impossible to quantify that benefit, but it is significant that the entry of the Tornado into service was much less traumatic than that of the F-111 and the European aircraft has had a far better safety record. Bureaucratic inflexibility too imposed extra delays

Right:
In February 1985 carriage and jettison tests of the British Aerospace ALARM defence suppression missile began from Warton. Here ZA354 is seen carrying nine ALARM shapes together with a Skyshadow and a BOZ pod.

and costs on the programme. Martin Steinberger cited the development of the RB199 engine as an example of this:

'In such a programme one should strive for the ultimate, but not believe one will necessarily achieve it. There needed to be somebody with authority to trade development costs against performance targets, but in the case of Tornado that did not happen. We [Turbo-Union] had to continue developing the engine for a year, during 1978-79, to obtain the final 1½% of specified thrust before it was cleared for production. That cost the governments a lot of money, at a time when we already had on the drawing board versions of the engine which would give 5% to 15% more thrust.

'I believe the early Tornados would have been just as good as they were if their maximum thrust had been 1½% less than it was. But we had to continue with the development of the engine because we had contractural obligations to achieve that level of thrust. Had it been a civilian contract I would have tried to persuade the customer to accept the lower thrust, and offered production engines at a lower price. In that case the RB199 would have cost less to develop, and the service units which received the initial Tornados would have had to incorporate far fewer engine modifications.

'The reason why the governments would not settle for a bit less thrust than specified was purely psychological. I worked with Rolls-Royce during the 1960s and I know how the British think. The British approach is for the company to offer 105% of what it thinks it can achieve, knowing that is impossible but hoping to get 100%. But if a customer asks for 100% he will probably get only 97%. In Germany and Italy the approach is different. If a company offers a certain performance level it is tied to that in the contract: even if an engine reaches 99% of the contracted performance, a very good achievement, development has to go on until 100% is achieved.

'In the case of the RB199 nobody had the authority to say "Let's stop here for now; we have an engine that looks good, it achieves 98½% of the contracted performance which is very good, let's put it into production". But we could not do that so we had a year of arguments and negotiations, just for that last 1½% engine thrust.'

The new 27mm cannon developed for the Tornado underwent a similarly wasteful process during attempts to bring it to perfection.

Bureaucratic inflexibility was a source of continual frustration during the Tornado programme, though in Peter Liddell's view even it had a positive side:

'We in industry are very nervous about changes to the basic requirements of an aircraft once it is in the design or construction stage. If the customer keeps changing his mind it can be disastrous — that was one reason for the cost overrun that led to the downfall of the TSR2. That can happen with a national programme. But with an international programme it is very much more difficult for one nation's enthusiasts to make changes to the aircraft. An international programme imposes a degree of stability on itself which can have very positive effects, I think that is one reason why we were able to do as well as we did within the cost constraints of the Tornado.'

When reviewing those aspects of the Tornado programme which did not work well, it is important to separate those which resulted from the multinational project from those which would also have been present in any European national programme. It is a fact that European companies take somewhat longer to design, build and test a new combat aircraft than is the case for American companies. There are several reasons for this. An American company will often adopt multi-shift working and take on extra labour if it needs to speed a programme, knowing it can resume single shift working afterwards and sack those workers it no longer needs; such practices are not usual in Europe. Flight testing of a combat aircraft takes much longer in Europe because governments order far fewer prototypes than would be the case in an equivalent American programme: there were only 11 prototype and development Tornados, compared with 23 F-111s.

Asked for his comments on the Tornado programme as a whole, and the lessons he thought it held for the future of the European aircraft industry, General Heinz Birkenbeil said:

'We should not fall into the trap of looking at the programme from a purely negative viewpoint, saying "This, this and this did not work. So next time let us do it in a completely different way". We must bear in mind that the Tornado is a very effective combat aeroplane, and it has been built within budget allowing for inflation. Every part of it worked from the first flight — which is very rare for an advanced combat aeroplane. We never had to ground the aircraft during the test phase because of a major failure, everything worked well enough and safely enough. There were some problems with the engines but we never had a disaster, during the test programme we didn't lose a single aeroplane for that reason.

'We should look at those aspects of the aircraft that worked, then look at those that didn't work. We should investigate why various aspects of the management didn't work well enough, and do those things better next time. But it would be silly to throw everything away and change the entire system, just because a few things did not work well the first time.'

Heinz Birkenbeil made his remarks prior to the decision, in June 1986, to go ahead with the multi-national Eurofighter aircraft programme. But his views appear to have been accepted by the British, German, Italian and Spanish governments: the management of the new programme will be along lines similar to those for Tornado. In its essentials that management process is sound, though the author would hope that the weaknesses in the former system can be overcome and the International Project Office controlling the development of the new aircraft will not become a mirror-image of NAMMA. As in any efficient management process, it is a question of choosing the right people and giving them the authority to do the job.

A much-quoted adage has it that 'Nothing is more inevitable than an idea whose time has come.' Since the end of World War 2 the nations of western Europe have come together, willingly, to an extent that could scarcely have been imagined before that conflict. Politically and militarily those nations have established bonds which are becoming stronger with each year that passes. Tornado succeeded because, for Europe, the time has come for the multi-national technical development programme. As Fausto Cereti of Aeritalia put it:

'Of course, the success of the Tornado is the result of much hard work and dedication from a lot of people. But in my view Tornado was not a success out of the blue, it was a product of its time. It is a demonstration that Europe was ready for this kind of achievement. At about the same time other European projects like the Ariane space programme and Airbus have also succeeded. It means the European environment is suitable for the exploitation of modern technology. Big things do not happen because a few people want them to, but because the environment is ready for them.'

Top left:
Seen here is the prototype installation of infra-red equipment in the fuselage of the Tornado, in place of the two 27mm cannon in the IDS version, which will equip the specialised reconnaissance version on order for two Royal Air Force squadrons. The fit comprises a British Aerospace Linescan 4000 (with sensor in the bulge under the fuselage) and a separate Sideways Looking Infra-Red (SLIR) system (with sensors behind a window on either side of the fuselage). Together these give horizon-to-horizon cover across track; their outputs can be displayed on a TV-type screen in the navigator's position, and are video-taped for subsequent analysis. This advanced infra-red system produces high-resolution imagery as good as that from optical cameras, and none of the latter will be carried in the RAF reconnaissance Tornado.

Centre left:
A model of the Electronic Combat & Reconnaissance (ECR) version of the Tornado ordered for the Luftwaffe. In place of the two 27mm cannon normally fitted to the IDS this aircraft will carry forward- and sideways-looking infra-red systems for reconnaissance, and an emitter-location equipment similar to that carried by USAF 'Wild Weasel' F-4s assigned to the defence suppression role. In a typical mission it is envisaged that one or two ECR Tornados would fly a few minutes ahead of a formation of attack Tornados, the ECR aircraft using their reconnaissance systems to locate moving targets such as enemy vehicles moving up to the battle area at night. The ECR aircraft would direct the attack Tornados on to such targets, at the same time using their anti-radiation missiles to suppress enemy air defence systems in the area. The model carries two HARM (High Speed Anti-Radiation Missiles) under the fuselage and four SRARM (Short Range Anti-Radiation Missiles) or ASRAAM (Advanced Short Range Air-to-Air Missiles) on the inboard wing pylons.

Bottom left:
To provide defence suppression during attacks on enemy warships, the German Navy has ordered HARM for its IDS Tornados. Aircraft 98+60 is seen carrying four HARM shapes during carriage and jettison trials; a more likely operational load would be a pair of HARM under the fuselage and the normal arrangement of tanks, self-protection air-to-air missiles and ECM pods on the wing pylons.

Appendix

Paul Millett's report of the first flight of the MRCA.

FLIGHT REPORT

Date: 14.8.1974	Aircraft: MRCA P01	Flight: No 1
Pilot: Millett, P.	Crew: Meister, N.	Test Schedule: No 65
Location: Manching	Take-off: 17.21hr	Flight Time: 33mins
Weather: Clear and calm	Surface wind: 270/5	Temp: +30°

Test objectives:
Initial handling tests in approach configuration and clean aircraft up to 300kt.

Aircraft standard:
Configuration: Clean aircraft, full CSAS and all systems operative.
Loading: Total fuel: 3,760kg;
Total weight: 17,350kg; CG: 21.9%

Summary:
The aircraft was climbed in the approach configuration to 10,000ft, low speed handling checks made down to 160kt, then undercarriage and flaps brought in and clean aircraft handling checks made up to 300kt, in accordance with the planned programme. Manoeuvre flaps were operated during the descent and an overshoot and landing carried out.

Aircraft handling qualities were excellent at all conditions tested and the engines and systems behaved well, with the exception of an air conditioning failure.

FLIGHT DETAILS

Start-up and taxy
The aircraft was positioned on the taxyway close to the runway. APU and engine starts were normal.

During the short taxy to the end of the runway, normal and emergency brake checks were made and reverse thrust operated momentarily.

Take-off with mid flap
Fuel FWD 1,640kg, AFT 1,900kg.
The engines were opened up to maximum reheat before brake release. Acceleration was fairly brisk and by 120kt the aircraft was already feeling light on the nosewheel with the stick neutral. Rotation was started at 140kt and the aircraft flown off at 165kt. Aircraft attitude control was stable and positive throughout the rotation and when the aircraft became airborne the impression of a good firm positive control about all axes was immediately apparent. No trim changes were noted on unstick (tailplane — 4½°).

Climb
A nose up attitude about 12° was established to maintain a climb out speed of 200kt with undercarriage and mid flap using maximum reheat. Control remained good in all axes with excellent damping. The aircraft was buffet free and the noise level was low.

At about 3,000ft reheat was reduced to an intermediate setting (nozzles 56/57%) and the climb continued. Switching on cabin conditioning produced a small increase in the general noise level, most noticeable as extraneous noise picked up on the crew's microphones. When speed was reduced a very mild airframe buffet appeared below 190kt.

Handling at 10,000ft
At 10,000ft the reheats were cancelled one at a time and the aircraft stabilised at 200kt, 6.5° ADD, in level flight. The calibrated chase aircraft speed was 203kt. Aircraft response in pitch was slightly lower than expected but was nevertheless good. Stick forces were pleasant. Roll response was excellent. The rudder was powerful producing a flat yaw with only a small induced roll. Damping from stick jerks and rudder kicks was excellent. Some small yawing was induced during rolling manoeuvres.

Airspeed was reduced to 180kt (178kt at 9.5° ADD for 176kt chase aircraft) requiring 84%rpm to hold level flight. A very mild airframe buffet was apparent with a slight increase in buffet during nose-up pitching manoeuvres. The CSI was fluctuating ±15kt as the aircraft was pitching, but the 2 needle ASI fed from the main probe was steady.

A further reduction to 160kt was made to check approach handling (185kt at 12° ADD for 159kt chase aircraft). Buffet levels were still low. Roll response was reduced by 25%-30% but was still quite adequate for approach handling. Pitch response was virtually unchanged and the rudder remained very powerful. Damping in all axes remained excellent.

The right throttle was selected to maximum reheat. Reheat lit in about 3sec then modulated to maximum in 4 or 5 steps. No significant yawing was noticed. Reheat was cancelled as soon as maximum nozzle was reached and the speed stabilised at 200kt. The undercarriage was retracted successfully taking 4-5sec and producing no trim change.

Flaps were selected up at 220kt and the aircraft allowed to continue accelerating as the flaps retracted. A slight pilot-induced overcontrolling occurred at this time masking any small trim changes.

The airspeed was stabilised at 250kt (chase 250kt). Engine power was 82.8/82.5% NH. A small amplitudency low frequency (about 10Hz) vertical oscillation of the front fuselage started as the flaps came in. Nose down pitching of the aircraft slightly increased this oscillation and nose-up pitching decreased it. Pitch control and damping remained good. Roll response was crisp; yawing response to rudder deflection was noticeably reduced. Some slight yawing (±3°) was again noticed during roll entries and reversals and damping in all axes remained excellent.

Speed was increased to 300kt (chase 300kt for aircraft 299kt) using throttle settings of 83.8/83.4 NH. Fuel state at this time was 2,190kg. The fuselage oscillation was slightly increased but was still at a very low amplitude. Handling was excellent with slightly improved response in pitch and roll and less induced (±1° only in roll reversals). Normal acceleration was increased at 2g in a level turn with an incidence of 8.3° ADD and a decrease in the vertical bouncing motion, but no significant airframe buffet. 90% rpm was selected increasing the speed to 312kt in the turn.

Descent

Airspeed was reduced to 260kt and manoeuvre flap selected. No trim change or buffet occurred. Leaving throttles at idle, the aircraft was descended back to the airfield while carrying out gentle handling in the manoeuvre configuration without problem at speeds between 250kt and 290kt. Manoeuvre flap was selected in and an airfield flyover made at 310kt.

Circuit handling

Mid flap was selected at 235kt, 8° ADD, giving a small nose down trim change. By the time mid-flap was reached the airspeed was 220kt, 6° ADD. Undercarriage was selected down at 200kt, coming down cleanly without trim change. At 188kt power was 86% for level flight and the fuselage oscillation had again disappeared. Fuel state was 1,975kg.

The aircraft was flown around base leg at 175kt and the speed reduced to 165kt for the straight final approach. The aircraft felt exceptionally stable on the approach with excellent speed stability and control. 76%rpm gave 1,000ft/min rate of descent at 165kt, 11.5° ADD.

An overshoot was made using maximum dry power with a 2,000ft/min rate of climb at 190kt. After turning downwind the airspeed was settled at 180kt, which was found to be a comfortable circuit handling speed. Fuel state was FWD 78kg, AFT 1,000kg.

The final approach was flown at 160kt, (2° ADD using 83%rpm) and the excellent impression of handling gained from the first approach was confirmed.

Landing

When close to the runway the engines were throttled back to idle but the aircraft showed a strong tendency to float. At about 150kt the aircraft was put gently on the runway, the nosewheel lowered and nosewheel steering engaged. Reverse thrust was selected at about 140kt and power slowly increased from idle. Gentle braking was started at 100kt and power stabilised at 80% N3. Braking was increased to moderate at 90kt, at about 60kt the re-ingestion warning light came on and power reduced to idle, then reverse thrust was cancelled at about 20kt. Little difficulty was found in keeping the aircraft straight on the runway.

In dispersal, the fuel state was FWD 720kg, AFT 960kg, Total 1,705kg. Tank fuel temperature was 50° and the brakes 460°/350°.

Environmental control system

During flight the cabin conditioning flow dropped suddenly to a low level accompanied with a whistling noise from behind the cockpit. Emergency ram air was selected and the noise stopped. Later in the flight air conditioning was reselected on. The flow came back at a very low level without accompanied noise but the noise re-appeared after about 3min. Emergency ram air was reselected and left on subsequently.

Aircraft systems

Other than environmental control and standby pitot static system, all aircraft systems behaved perfectly. Radio communication with the chase aircraft, telemetry and air traffic control was excellent throughout.

Some telemetry drop-outs in turns were reported.

CONCLUSIONS

Stability and control

The aircraft handling was excellent throughout the flight, circuit handling and control of the approach and landing was exceptional. Although the flight was made in smooth air, the aircraft damping felt good enough to cope even with severe conditions. Some improvement to roll/yaw coupling at low speed may be necessary, but this is only a minor problem.

Buffet and vibration

With flaps and undercarriage down the aircraft was virtually buffet free at low incidence with only mild buffet appearing as incidence increased.

The clean aircraft had a vertical oscillation of very small amplitude at about the fuselage natural frequency. This oscillation will not constitute an aircraft problem unless the amplitude is greatly increased by change of configuration, speed or turbulence.

Noise levels were low.

Pitot-static system

Airspeed errors from the main probe were negligible but a ±15kt oscillation from the standby probe showed that some development is necessary in this area.

RECOMMENDATIONS

The fire extinguisher buttons should be replaced in a position where they are more easily visible from the normal pilot's eye position.

AIRCRAFT DEFECTS

1. Air conditioning flow dropped to a low level accompanied by a loud whistle.
2. Left engine throttle control difficult to change from Lane 2 to Lane 1.
3. CSI varies ±15kt in pitching oscillations.

(signed)

P. Millett.

Tornado GR1 43+35 of JaboG 38.
Ben Ullings

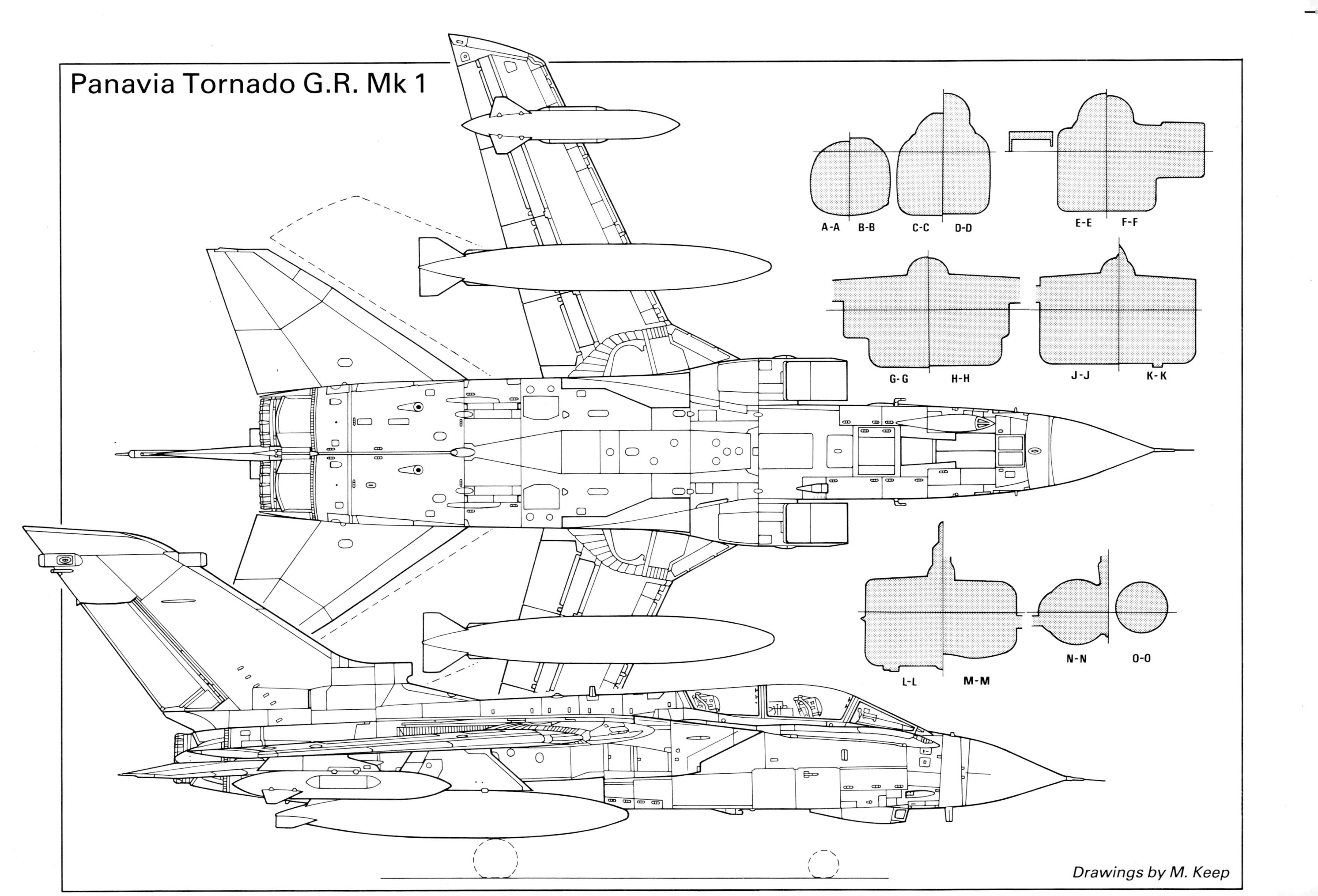
Panavia Tornado G.R. Mk 1
A-A
B-B
C-C
D-D
E-E
F-F
G-G
H-H
J-J
K-K
L-L
M-M
N-N
O-O
Drawings by M. Keep